CHEMICAL ENGINEERING
IN THE COAL INDUSTRY

CHEMICAL ENGINEERING

IN THE

COAL INDUSTRY

AN INTERNATIONAL CONFERENCE
organized by the National Coal Board, Great Britain
and held at its Coal Research Establishment
at Stoke Orchard, Cheltenham, England
in June 1956

Edited by
FORBES W. SHARPLEY

PERGAMON PRESS

LONDON   NEW YORK   PARIS

Published by Pergamon Press Ltd., 4 & 5 Fitzroy Square, London W.1.
122 East 55th Street, New York 22, N.Y.
24 Rue des Écoles, Paris Vᵉ.

Printed in Great Britain by Page Bros. (Norwich) Ltd.

CONTENTS

OPENING ADDRESS

By A. H. A. WYNN,
Member, National Coal Board

GENTLEMEN, it is my privilege today to open this conference on " Chemical Engineering in the Coal Industry "; it is my pleasure to welcome all the guests of the National Coal Board, from this country and from overseas. We are delighted to have so many delegates from overseas. This is the first conference to be held in these very new laboratories; this conference and the new laboratories are both a symbol of the National Coal Board's belief in the contribution that science has to make to this great industry.

The governments of western Europe—I think every Government of western Europe—have been studying very anxiously the energy resources on which their economies are to develop and that study has proceeded in particular detail during the last 12 months. There have been a number of publications in this country and abroad, on the coal resources and other energy resources of western Europe. The recently published report of the Energy Commission of the Organization for European Economic Co-operation is perhaps the most authoritative study of the energy problem in western Europe in the coming years.

All these estimates, official and unofficial, have come to the conclusion that the economy of western Europe will be dependent fundamentally upon the prosperity and technical progress of the coal industry during the next 20 or 30 years. The National Coal Board has recently had a delegation in Russia; there was one conclusion in their report that impressed me most. The further economic development of Russian industry is based expressly and fundamentally upon a plan for coal, that is, upon the expansion of the coal industry. The Russian economy is not to be based primarily upon oil, natural gas, or upon atomic energy, although these other sources of energy are under active development. Britain led the industrial revolution by developing her coal industry; the Russians in the twentieth century are developing their economy on the same foundation.

The technologist has two great tasks, to promote progress in the methods of coal production and to promote the more efficient use of coal. If the estimates of western Europe's future coal requirements are sound, then it is also true that there is little possibility of their achievement without great advances in the technologies of both coal production and utilization. The necessary technical progress is possible, but is it being sufficiently actively pursued?

The chemical engineer has yet to make his full contribution to the efficient utilization of coal. The French have invented a word " valorisation ", for which there is no strict equivalent in the English language. I think perhaps we should anglicize this useful word. Valorization may be defined as the business of making the best economic use of everything brought out of coal mines. Coal mining produces a great range of products. The ordinary consumer of coals may just regard them as black stones which burn, and black stones which do not burn. He is not aware that there are many different kinds of coal and associated minerals. At one end of the scale, there are the materials of low calorific value, the shales and clays that are an inevitable byproduct of mining. These are used by the National Coal Board to make bricks and other clay products; access to these byproducts of mining gave the brick industry a natural advantage in the coalfields that has made the coal industry one of the largest producers of bricks in the country. At the other end of the scale, there are the coals of the highest calorific value that are put to the best use by the carbonization industry.

Between these two extremes there is a wide range of materials brought out of our mines, including the low-rank noncaking coals and coals of more or less high ash content. There is a wide range of uses for these coals but much bituminous coal is burnt wastefully; the smoke that pollutes the atmosphere is visible evidence of this waste. It is by promoting the valorization of this coal that this conference can make its contribution.

Here at the Coal Research Establishment, we are particularly concerned with producing new improved fuels. We have devoted our attention to producing new products of carbonization and to extending the range of coals suitable for carbonization. In some parts of the country, there is a shortage of the best carbonization coals and it is therefore important that we should make use of coals of lower rank which are cheaper to mine, for the manufacture of coke and coke briquettes. You will have the opportunity to see the work of the laboratories and will note the emphasis on the valorization of coals which are not the best carbonization coals.

There is much progress to be made in determining the best use of coals that are not in the premium class, of weakly caking coals, low-rank coals and coals of high ash and sulphur content. We can no longer afford only to mine reserves of the very best coals and, if we are to achieve the maximum output of energy, we must develop new processes and new equipment to make full use of coal that is not of the very best quality but of which there are ample reserves.

I believe that some of our economic problems in western Europe are due to our neglect of our basic industries. We shall only succeed in overcoming this neglect if there are enough young men joining the basic industries who are convinced of the great scope for the application of modern science and engineering to their problems. It is important for us to inform the young men in our schools and universities what a wide range of exciting and interesting new scientific and technical problems there are to be solved, and to make it clear to the new generation what a responsibility will be on their shoulders to promote the technical progress of the coal industry.

I conclude, gentlemen, by offering my very best wishes and the best wishes of the National Coal Board for the success of this conference on " Chemical Engineering in the Coal Industry ".

CONTROLLED OXIDATION OF COAL

By A. F. BOYER

Centre d'Études et Recherches des Charbonnages de France, Verneuil, France

Summary—Preliminary oxidation of coal is probably justified only in a very small number of cases. Nevertheless, examples are given of the industrial processes used in France, in those instances where oxidation before the carbonization or combustion process appears to be worthwhile.

The paper then summarizes three investigations:

1. A description of two semi-industrial scale tests of oxidation of coking coal in a fluidized bed, with a throughput of 100 kg/hr (200 lb./hr).

3. Laboratory study of the fixation of oxygen by coal. The reaction was studied between 160°C and 240°C, the parameter investigated being the variation in weight. This made it possible to determine an energy of activation of 15 kcal/mole for a carefully-controlled oxidation.

Some details are given of the comparison of the behaviour of the natural coal and the oxidized coal during coking; this study covered the release of volatile matter, the emission of oxygen, the plasticity, the swelling and other coking properties.

3. A description is given of a process for the drying of a coking coal blend, using hot oxidizing gases without alteration of the coking properties. This process has been in operation for several years on a scale of 6 tons/hour.

Résumé—L'oxydation préalable du charbon ne se justifie probablement que dans un trés petit nombre de cas. On donne cependant des exemples de procédés industriels utilisés en France dans lesquels l'oxydation avant carbonization ou combustion paraît utile.

La communication résume ensuite trois études:

1. Description de deux essais semi-industriels d'oxydation de charbon gras en lît fluidisé à l'échelle 100 kg/heure.

2. Étude en laboratoire de la fixation d'oxygène sur du charbon. La réaction a été étudiée entre 160 et 240°C par variation de poids, ce qui a permis de déterminer une énergie d'activation de 15 kcal/mole pour une oxydation très ménagée.

On donne quelques précisions sur le comportement comparé des charbons naturels et des charbons oxydés au cours de la cokéfaction (départ des matières volatiles, de l'oxygène, plasticité, gonflement et autres propriétés cokéfiantes).

3. Procédé de séchage de fines à coke par fumées oxydantes chaudes, sans altération des propriétés cokéfiantes, qui fonctionne depuis quelques années a l'échelle 6 tonnes/heure.

Zusammenfassung—Eine Vorbehandlung der Kohle mit Sauerstoff dürfte nur in sehr seltenen Fällen angebracht sein. Der Verfasser gibt jedoch einige Beispiele aus der betrieblichen Praxis in Frankreich, wo die Oxydation der Kohle vor ihrer Verkokung, Schwelung oder Verbrennung zweckmässig erscheint. Sodann wird in knapper Form über drei Untersuchungen berichtet.

1. Beschreibung zweier Versuche der Oxydation von Fettkohle im Wirbelbett, mit einer Durchsatzleistung von 100 kg/h.

2. Laboratoriumsversuche über Aufnahme von Sauerstoff durch die Kohle.

Die Reaktion wurde zwischen 160 und 240°C untersucht. Durch Beobachtung der Gewichtsveränderung wurde bei sehr massvoller Oxydation eine Aktivierungsenergie von 15 kcal/Mol ermittelt. Der Vortrag enthält nähere Angaben über das unterschiedliche Verhalten von natürlichen Kohlen und von oxydierten Kohlen während des Verkokungsprozesses (Entweichen der flüchtigen Bestandteile und des Sauerstoffs, Plastizität, Blähvermögen und weitere Verkokungseigenschaften).

3. Trocknung einer Kokerei-Einsatzkohle durch heisse, sauerstoffhaltige Rauchgase ohne Veränderung der Verkokungseigenschaften; dieses Verfahren wird seit einigen Jahren in der Praxis angewandt (Durchsatzleistung 6 t/h).

I. WHY OXIDIZE COAL?

THE industrial oxidation of coals is frequently proposed as a means of reducing their caking properties. We will cite two cases (Bruay and Carmonoix) where experience has proved the necessity for pretreatment: at Bruay it is required to ensure that carbonization does not cause caking of the fines, while at Carmaux it is intended to prevent agglomeration of domestic briquettes. A number of processes for rapid carbonization or for gasification are under development; in all these processes the adhesion of coal particles to one another raises a difficulty.

We cannot make such definite statements with regard to semicarbonization in a fluidized bed. There is no doubt that the particularly rapid heating involved in this process causes fusion of coals which are normally considered to have a low caking power. But in the 100 kg/hr (200 lb./hr) plant at Verneuil we have been able to semicarbonize—without any preoxidation—all the coals which we have subjected to test; among these there are a gas-coking coal from Bruay—with 33% of volatiles in the pure coal substance—and a gas-coking coal from Camphausen—with 35% volatiles (swelling index 8 to 9, Gray-King class G_6). The transition to a larger scale, in the 1000 kg/hr (1 ton/hr) plant at Marienau, gave rise to several small difficulties, in spite of the fact that the coal treated has a very low caking power (swelling index 2); however, we have not yet examined the possibility that certain fluidization conditions would eliminate these difficulties.

It is, in fact, quite certain that the point where the coal is introduced into the bed, the turbulence of the fluidized bed, and the presence or absence of a grid, have a considerable influence on the risk of caking. Thus, at the time of writing (February 1956), we do not yet know if previous oxidation is necessary for semicarbonization in a fluidized bed or not.

In addition to the action of air, there are other methods of bringing about a reduction in coking power; we shall not go into details of these methods here, as their technical foundation is very different. Certain studies have been carried out in France—at Carmaux[1] and at Cerchar[2]—on such methods as the incorporation of sulphur (approximately 0·5%). The action is entirely comparable to that of oxygen. The treatment is very simple, since it merely involves making a mixture before carbonization is carried out, but it is obviously only applicable in certain special cases—e.g. the carbonization of briquettes—and has no interest in connection with carbonization in a fluidized bed.

Another aspect of this problem is met with in the industrial drying of blends for coking; here the problem is the reverse of the previous one, in that it involves heating the coal without changing its coking properties.

Finally, we may think of applying oxidation to reduce the formation of tar during combustion (and, as a result, also reducing the emission of smoke, as in the " Anthracine " process); or again as a means of transforming the coal into " humic acids ", when the chemical industry becomes interested in using these products.

II. INDUSTRIAL APPLICATION IN FRANCE

1. *Production of Domestic Fuel at Carmaux*[3]

This particular manufacturing process was begun twenty years ago; more than 100 tons of coking coal, with 28% to 30% of volatiles, are treated daily.

In the " Carmonoix " process—which is the most widely used at the moment—dried fines are briquetted, in the shape of balls weighing 20 grams, using 5 % of pitch. These balls are loaded into a kind of basket which holds 3 tons, and are then placed in tanks, through which oxidizing gases are passed at a temperature of 160°C to 170°C. Since the oxidation is exothermic, cooling is carried out by blowing cooler air through the tanks from time to time.

After roughly 10 hours of treatment the balls have lost approximately 2 % of their original weight. They have still sufficient caking power to allow them to be carbonized; however, there is no risk of their swelling or caking together, as would be the case with untreated balls.

2. *Manufacture of Semicoke at Bruay*[4]

At Bruay, the semicoke manufactured is intended for mixing with very strongly fusing coals—having 28 % to 33 % volatiles—for coking purposes. This semicoke is prepared by heating coals of average fusibility in an inclined rotating furnace, made of sheet steel; the swelling index of these coals is from 3 to 5, and they would cake together if they were not oxidized.

The preheating and the oxidation are both carried out in inclined rotating furnaces, which are heated to about 300°C by means of the gases which have already served to heat the semicarbonization furnaces. A slight current of air passes through the furnace. The treatment is checked by means of an " index of agglutination ".

The same technique of semicarbonization is used at Marienau in the Lorraine coalfield, where it is not necessary to preoxidize the coal, because its coking properties are very slight (swelling index from 1 to 2).

3. *Manufacture of Briquettes with Reduced Smoke Production by the " Anthracine 54 " Process*

The oxidation is used here as a means of reducing the smoke formed when the briquetted balls are burned. This production process is in full development.

The briquettes are made from a dry steam coal with approximately 10 % of volatiles, using pitch. The oxidation process resembles that used at Carmaux, but the plant is more modern. The briquettes are loaded into wagons with a grid bottom, these wagons running in a tunnel furnace.

Hot oxidizing gases are blown in from the bottom; the temperature of these gases is adjusted so that it does not exceed 320°C to 350°C after having passed through the layer of briquettes. If the reaction gets out of hand, water spraying is resorted to.

The oxidation takes about 4 hours. It is necessary to cool off the briquettes before they are exposed to the air. The above treatment is much more effective than would be the maintaining of the briquettes at 350°C in the absence of air.

III. SEMI-INDUSTRIAL TESTS AT CERCHAR

We carried out at Verneuil two experiments on the oxidation of fines in a fluidized bed, using the 100 kg/hr (200 lb./hr) semicarbonization retort which was described in a publication by M. Foch (no grid, with stirrer rotating at 133 rev./min).

The coal used was a gas-coking coal from Bruay, having the following analysis: 10·9 % ash; 30·4 % volatiles; 6·0 % oxygen (on a dry coal basis) and 2 % of moisture.

The swelling index was 7·5; the size distribution was $20\% < 0.1$ mm and $80\% < 0.5$ mm.

First Trial

A quantity of 37 Nm³/hr (1200 s.c.f./hr) of air at 375°C was blown through the retort; this corresponds to a normal turbulent fluidization, with an average time of residence in the retort of approximately 10 minutes. The temperature of the bed was from 225°C to 250°C.

After the first passage, the swelling index dropped from 7·5 to 2·5; after a second passage it fell from 2·5 to 1·25. The oxygen content rose by approximately 3%.

Second Trial

Here the flow of air was 20 m³/hr (710 cu. ft./hr), a quantity just sufficient to give a fluidized bed; the temperature of the air was 240°C. The temperature of the bed became stabilized around 220°C; the flow of coal was very low and the average residence time (which was not measured) might have been approximately 30 minutes.

In a single passage, the oxygen content rose by almost 2%; the swelling index fell to 2·25 and was no higher than 1·5 after a few days of storage at atmospheric temperature.

Trials with carbonization in a fluidized bed, using hot gases to heat the oxidized coal, at temperatures ranging from 450°C to 650°C, have showed that, by comparison with the untreated coal:

(a) the bulk density of the semicoke obtained was lower (0·10 instead of 0·15 at 650°C and 0·33 instead of 0·37 at 460°C),

(b) for a quantity of 100 kg (220 lb.) of dry coal, we obtained during a trial with carbonization at 550°C, 73 kg (161 lb.) of semicoke (instead of 68 kg (150 lb.), but only 12·9 kg (28·4 lb.) of moisture-free dedusted tar (instead of 22·3 kg (49·1 lb.)).

Since the carbonization of the untreated coal presented no difficulties, and as we prefer to have a fairly high bulk density for the semicoke, it was considered preferable not to continue oxidation. We did, nevertheless, establish that—in case of need—it would be very simple to use this technique to destroy the coking properties. The very homogeneous distribution of temperature in a fluidized bed would allow of oxidation at a higher temperature—and therefore of greater efficiency—without any risk of ignition.

IV. LABORATORY WORK ON OXIDATION

1. Kinetics of the Reaction

This problem has been investigated by other laboratories of the Charbonnages de France.[5, 6, 7] We ourselves carried out several trials in 1953, using the coking coal from Bruay; these trials were carried out at the same time as the semi-industrial tests described in the previous paragraph. The object of our investigation was to measure the variations in the initial speed of oxidation in the presence of excess air as a function of temperature.

a) Experimental method. 600 mg of coal of normal industrial size distribution are placed in a thin layer on the pan of a Chevinard thermal balance. The temperature is kept constant (between 160°C and 240°C in our tests) and a slight air flow is allowed to pass by natural draught, sufficient to maintain a large excess of air. The increase in weight is recorded as a function of time (Fig. 1); the test is stopped after several hours and the oxygen content of the sample determined.

   b) *Relationship between oxidation and increase in weight.* There is, first of all, fixation of oxygen in the coal, followed by evolution of the oxidation products. In the general case, therefore, the increase in weight has no simple relationship with

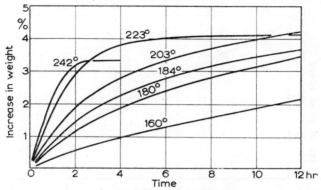

FIG. 1—Increase in weight caused by oxidation of Coal (Bruay 1529)
in air between 160°C and 240°C.

the quantity of oxygen which has entered into the reaction and all that can be said is that it is equal to or less than the latter. We have, however, established that, for a low degree of oxidation, the increase in weight is not much less than the increase in oxygen content of the sample, as determined by elementary analysis (Table 1); consequently, we may hope that the *initial rate* of increase in weight gives a correct measure of the initial rate of oxidation.

   On the other hand, for a stronger degree of oxidation the observed increases in weight and quantities of oxygen consumed show that some carbon or hydrogen has been gasified (Table 1). The shape of the curves at high temperature in Fig. 1 confirms this, a tendency to increase in weight being evident towards the end.

TABLE 1

Conditions of oxidation of the coal	Oxygen content %	Weight increase assuming only fixation occurs	Weight increase observed
Not oxidized	6·0	0	0
Slight oxidation 6 hr at 204°C 12 hr at 160°C	10·0 8·5	4·0 2·5	3·9 2·15
Strong oxidation 72 hr at 184°C 72 hr at 203°C	16·5 17·0	10·5 11·0	6·1 4·6

It has also been confirmed that the curves do not vary greatly with the thickness of the coal layer on the pan; the particles were quite accessible to the air.

c) Results. The experimental results are plotted in Figs. 1 and 2. In particular, it can be seen that the initial rate of increase in weight varies with temperature in accordance with Arrhenius's equation, with a corresponding activation energy of 15·2 kcal/mole.

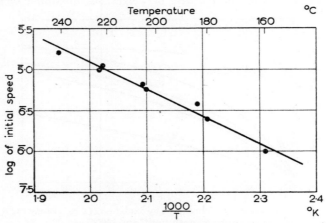

FIG. 2—Variations in the initial speed of oxidation with temperature; coal (Bruay 1529) in air.

These measurements completely confirm the advantage of working at relatively high temperatures to produce rapid oxidation. The important zone, from the point of view of the destruction of coking properties, corresponds to fixation of from 1% to 2% of oxygen.

On the question of oxidation speeds, it is as well to point out that certain low temperature semicokes (450°C—500°C) oxidize much more easily than the corresponding coal. This is perhaps due to the increase in porosity following carbonization.

It also seems that in the case of Lorraine coals, which we have more specially studied, the vitrain oxidizes more easily than the dull coal; this arises from a difference in properties between the two fundamental constituents of the latter: vitrinite and exinite.

2. *Influence of Oxidation on Coking*

The oxidation of gas-coking coals modifies their characteristics, generally in the same way as the characteristics change in passing from a coal of low oxygen content to a coal of higher oxygen content but with the same volatile content. The majority of these modifications are well known; we shall, however, give some examples:

a) The discharge of volatile matter in the zone of rapid pyrolysis. Fig. 3 shows from an actual example, that the oxidation tends to spread the thermal decomposition over a wider temperature range.

The maximum speed of emission of volatile matter is thus always reduced by oxidation. The same fact is observed in the study of natural coals of different oxygen

contents. In Lorraine, for example, there are several types of coal of about 37%
volatile matter:—
    — gas-coking coal B with 8% oxygen;
    — long-flame gas-coking coal with 9% oxygen;
    — other long-flame gas-coking coals with more than 10% oxygen.
The maximum rate of loss of weight for a heating rate of 2°C per minute goes down

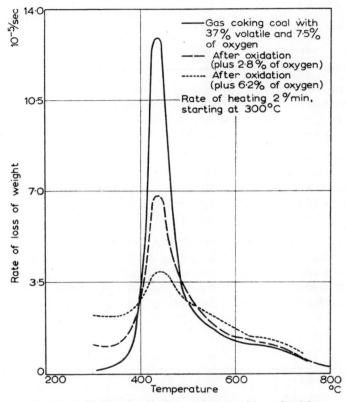

FIG. 3—Influence of oxidation on the rate of loss of weight.

from 13×10^{-5} per second in the first case to 11×10^{-5} in the second case and 10×10^{-5} in the third. With some lignites of 40% to 42% volatile matter still lower maximum rates are found.

This property has the following consequence, which seems quite unexpected: in certain cases the maximum rate of discharge of combined oxygen in the volatile matter can *decrease* after oxidation of the coal. The maximum discharge of oxygen practically coincides in fact with that of the volatile matter.[11]

On the other hand, the emission of volatile matter and combined oxygen is more rapid for an oxidized coal above 500°C.

b) Emission of volatile matter above 500°C. We have examined more carefully what occurs above 500°C, by comparing some semicokes of both fresh and oxidized coals prepared at the same temperatures:

(*i*) Characteristics of coals used.

Type of coal	Volatile matter content % (on original) (AFNOR)	Crucible swelling index	Ash content on dry basis	Elementary analysis (on original)			
				Carbon %	Hydro-gen %	Oxy-gen %	Sul-phur %
Lorraine gas-coking Coal B	38·0	7	2·3	85·0	5·5	8·6	0·4
Aquitaine gas-coking Coal	28·3	9	4·5	88·0	5·2	4·5	0·4

(*ii*) Oxidation. The coals, ground to 0·16 mm, were kept in air at 100°C—105°C, in thin layers. The gas-coking coal B contained 13·2% oxygen after 32 hours and 14% after 64 hours; the Aquitaine gas-coking coal contained 6·3% after 34 hours and 7·8% after 78 hours.

(*iii*) Carbonization and analysis. The carbonization was carried out in the absence of air at a heating rate of 2°C per minute, with sudden cooling immediately the desired temperature had been reached. The normal sample and the two corresponding oxidized samples were heated in the same metallic block to ensure identical thermal treatment.

The volatile-matter content was determined from a thermal gravimetric curve obtained at a heating rate of 2°C per minute. The volatile matter so determined is that which is actually freed during carbonization and is not contaminated by the gas which the coke could absorb by exposure to air. We thus regularly find a zero volatile-matter content for a coke heated to 1000°C.

TABLE 2

Lorraine Coking Coal B

Carbonization temperature	Normal sample		Sample oxidized for 32 hr		Sample oxidized for 64 hr	
	Volatile matter (on original) % at 2°C/min	Oxygen content (on original) %	Volatile matter (on original) % at 2°C/min	Oxygen content (on original) %	Volatile matter (on original) % at 2°C/min	Oxygen content (on original) %
Start	34·6	8·6	32·6	13·2	33	14
400°C	32·4	6·8	28	9·8	26·5	10·1
450°C	22·5	6·3	22·6	8·5	22	8·7
500°C	14·3	5·4	16·4	6·9	16·6	7·5
600°C	7·9	3·7	9·4	3·6	9·2	3·7
700°C	4	2·6	4·6	2·6	4·2	2·9

TABLE 3

Aquitaine Coking Coal

Carbonization temperature	Normal sample		Sample oxidized for 34 hr		Sample oxidized for 78 hr	
	Volatile matter (on original) % at 2°C/min	Oxygen content (on original) %	Volatile matter (on original) % at 2°C/min	Oxygen content (on original) %	Volatile matter (on original) % at 2°C/min	Oxygen content (on original) %
Start	24·4	4·5	24	6·3	23·7	7·8
400°C	22·9	4·7	21·9	5·1	20·8	6·1
450°C	18·9	4·5	18·8	5	18·1	6
500°C	11·9	3·9	13·6	4·1	13·5	4·8
600°C	6·7	3	7·7	3	7·9	3
700°C	3·5	2·4	4·2	2·4	4·1	2·5

(*iv*) Results. These are given in Tables 2 and 3. It can be seen that, at 500°C, the semicokes derived from the oxidized samples contain more oxygen and volatile matter than those derived from fresh coal. The difference disappears gradually after 600°C, but the major part of the " supplementary " oxygen which has been fixed is given off before 500°C.

TABLE 4

Coal	Treatment	Plastometer tests 2°C/min		
		Start of rotation °C	Max. speed degrees/min	End of rotation °C
Camphausen gas-coking A with 35% V.M.	coal not oxidized	363	1480	468
Swelling index 9	exposed for 20 hr to air after grinding	375	585	466
Dourges gas-coking with 25% V.M.	ground in absence of air to size 0·06 mm	366	8500	485
Swelling index 9	ground in air to 0·06 mm	370	5600	483
	ground in absence of air to 0·16 mm	368	8500*	485
	ground in air to 0·16 mm	370	8800*	484

* The difference is not significant.

c) The fusion of oxidized coals. It is well known that when a gas-coking coal is slightly oxidized the softening temperature rises and the fluidity (registered by the Gieseler plastometer or similar device) drops. Some examples are given in Tables 4 and 5, and in Fig. 4. This diagram shows the variations in maximum plasticity of three coals (*A*: gas-coking coal (Sarre) with 35% volatile matter; *B*: gas-coking coal (Lorraine) with 37%; *C*: long-flame gas-coking coal (Lorraine) with 37%) as a function of the time in air at the ambient temperature, with a particle size of less than 0·2 mm. Despite the considerable dispersion of the results for *A* and *B*, the general aspect of the phenomenon is not in doubt. Some analogous results established by oxidation at 105°C are quoted in Table 5.

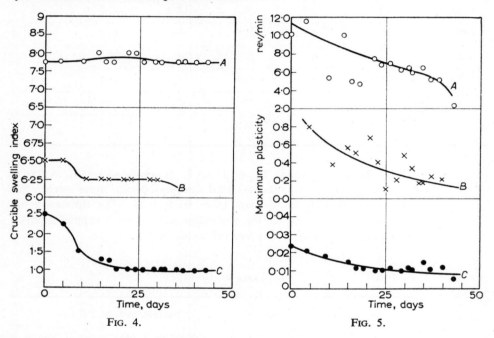

FIG. 4.   FIG. 5.

The effect on the swelling is more complex, because it happens that a very slight oxidation somewhat helps the tendency to swell in the case of certain very fusible coals of high volatile content. But in practically all cases a decrease in swelling is evident (Fig. 5).

d) Considerations on the inhibition of fusion. The oxidation of a coal is detectable by means of a plastometer, well before it shows up in ultimate analysis. We have tried to estimate it in the following way.

We have plotted the curve of oxygen fixation at 105°C, (as determined by ultimate analysis), over a period of about one hundred hours, for four gas-coking coals, with volatile contents ranging from 25% to 37%. This rate of fixation appeared to be nearly constant for each coal (8 hours were necessary to obtain a measurable increase of 0·5% in oxygen content for a coal of 37% volatile matter and 9% oxygen; 25 hours for a coal of 28% volatile matter and 5% oxygen; 30 to 40 hours for a coal of

TABLE 5

Modifications to a Gas-Coking Coal of 25% V.M. by Oxidation in Air at 105°C

Oxidation period (hours)	Oxygen content % on original	Crucible swelling index (AFNOR)	Dilatometric Test AFNOR 2°C/min					Plastometric Test GIESELER 2°C/min				Solidification temperature at 2°C/min °C
			Start of fusion °C	End of fusion °C	End of swelling °C	Contraction %	Swelling %	Start of rotation °C	End of rotation °C	Max. speed degrees/min	Fluidity zone (>10°/min) °C	
0	3·6	>9	375	420	478	32	212	365	483	4000 at 451°C	408–478	504
16		>9	375	422	478	33	143	370	480	207 at 452°C	423–470	501
32	4·2	9	375	434	478	32	99	370	471	48 at 444°C	423–450	501
48		8½	370	443	481	35	38	378	480	10 at 447°C		492
64	4·3	8	370	445	483	37	29	380	475	4 at 441°C		488
80		6	390	471	485	37	1					insufficient fusion to allow of measurement
96	4·6	5¼	390	495*	no swelling	17	0	426				—
112	5·5	1	395	ill-defined	—	ill-defined	0			rotation scarcely noticeable at about 430°		

* This is a conventional point on the dilatometric curve, and certainly no longer corresponds to a true "fusion".

25% volatile matter and 3·6% oxygen). *Assuming the rate has been the same during the first hours of oxidation* the quantity of fixed oxygen which lowers in a perceptible and definite manner the speed of rotation of the plastometer can be estimated to be 0·1%.

Some tests have likewise been made with sulphur, which is easy to incorporate in the coal in controlled quantities, by dissolving it in carbon disulphide. It appeared, very approximately, that 0·5% by weight of sulphur had an analogous inhibiting action on the fusion to that of 0·2% or 0·3% of oxygen.

It is not in the least surprising that rheology enables us to detect the influence of one atom of oxygen or sulphur on 1000 carbon atoms. The " molecules " in the molten coal are certainly of sufficiently great weight, and contain, at least, some 50 carbon atoms. If each oxygen atom has formed a " bridge " between two separate molecules, then we have an increase in the average molecular weight of the order of 10%, sufficient to explain the small increase in viscosity produced by 0·1% oxygen.

The influence on the temperature of incipient fusion is also very sensitive, and shows that the fixed oxygen acts on the coal below 350°C, in a zone where pyrolysis has not yet been indicated by any appreciable emission of volatile matter.

e) Tendency of the coke to fissuration. The temperature of resolidification after fusion drops slightly after oxidation, but is generally less affected than the temperature at which fusion begins. The result is that the rate of contraction on resolidification—which governs the degree of fissuration of the coal [8, 9]—is not effected much by slight oxidation.

In the case of a pure coal, however, a certain unfavourable action is evident. Thus we have seen the maximum rate of contraction of a good coking coal increases from 5 to 6·5 × 10⁻⁴ per degree for a very strong oxidation which leaves hardly any coking power, and from 6 to 8 × 10⁻⁴ per degree for a coking coal of 28% volatile matter. The fissuration is only really troublesome above 8 × 10⁻⁴.

In the case of coal mixtures the question is much more complex and cannot be completely dealt with here. It can be foreseen, however, that in the case of a binary mixture of gas-coking coals the oxidation of the constituent having the higher temperature of solidification will always be unfavourable. For the other constituent, several opposing effects play a part, and probably almost balance each other out in a controlled oxidation.

f) Other oxidation effects. The tendency of the coke to become graphitized at about 2000°C is reduced; the optical anisotropy at about 1000°C is also reduced (reflecting power when observed between crossed nicols). At about 700°C, the semi-cokes of oxidized coals have a tendency to have slightly higher specific surfaces (Brunauer, Emmet, and Teller method).

It should be noticed that, in the case of a very carefully controlled hydrogenation, phenomena almost exactly the converse of those occurring in oxidation are observed.

g) Practical consequences. From this study we note two in particular:
    (*a*) For the test in the Gieseler Plastometer, we have discovered that it is preferable to grind the coal in the absence of air. The changes seem to be much

more rapid during grinding than when ground coal is exposed to the air at atmospheric temperatures.

(b) Bearing in mind the properties of coals oxidized at low temperatures, it cannot be expected that they will replace dry steam coal, semicoke or coke dust as " anti-fissurant " additives.

V. NONOXIDIZING DRYING OF COAL

This is the converse of the problem which we discussed in the beginning of this paper. In certain cases (preparation of metallurgical coke from coals with a high volatile content, in particular), better results are obtained on the industrial scale by charging the furnace with dry coal; this is certainly due, first, to the resulting increase in bulk density, and, then, perhaps because the temperature and pressure distributions in the furnace are better with a dry charge than with a tamped moist charge of the same density (as indicated by the degree of fissuring). An incidental result is that economies are achieved in the operation of the coke-oven plant, the screening and methodical grinding are considerably facilitated, and the quantity of condensation water produced is reduced.

But it is necessary to ensure drying the coal without oxidizing it, since the caking properties are favourable in this case. The study of drying was carried out between 1951 and 1953 at the experimental station at Marienau,[10] operated by Cerchar, and in particular, the trials were carried out with a coal which is very susceptible to oxidation; this was a long-flame gas-coking coal, with 36% of volatiles and a swelling index of 4 to 5.

Technique of Drying. The throughput is 6 tons/hour. The coal is ground in the wet state to below 3 mm. It is put through a Lessing dryer —a sort of vertical tube, fitted with baffles; the coal passes through in about 10 seconds, while the hot gases are circulated in countercurrent. Let T_1 be the temperature of the coal on leaving this dryer.

The dried fines are fed to a chain scraper, where they begin to cool off; this scraper carries them to a storage bunker, where the cooling continues, but much more slowly. T_2 is the temperature at the moment the coal enters into storage; T_2 is dependent on T_1 and also on the flow of cooling air which is fed over the chain scraper.

The drying is carried out by means of gases which have a marked oxidation effect; in point of fact, it is necessary to introduce a considerable excess of air so that these gases are not too hot. The temperature of the gases on entering varies from 300°C (T_1 about 80°C, T_2 about 45°C) to 700°C. (T_1 about 120°C, T_2 about 75°C).

Changes in the coal—The changes in the coal were studied in two ways: on the one hand, by carbonizing the coal in industrial furnaces and, on the other, by subjecting the coal to laboratory tests (plasticity, swelling).

The conclusions were supplemented by a series of laboratory tests in which the coal was submitted to a similar treatment.

During the drying proper (10 seconds in the hot oxidizing gases and a few minutes in contact with cold air in the chain scraper) no appreciable changes seem to have occurred. On the other hand, if the coal is stored for several days after being dried, the coking properties may fall off rapidly.

A systematic study showed that these changes depend above all on the temperature T_2, this being the temperature when the coal is put into storage. If T_2 equals 80°C, the deterioration is very marked after 50 hours of storage; if T_2 is brought down to approximately 45°C, no significant modifications in the coal occur over a period of several days. It would therefore seem that oxidation takes place, not during the short period when the coal is passing through the dryer, but rather during the period of some hours of contact between the coal and the air in the hoppers, where the temperature is between 40°C and 80°C.

The reduction in coking properties, when it takes place, is more noticeable in furnaces of 450 mm (17·7 in.) diameter than in those of 380 mm (15 in.) diameter. The rate of heating is, however, very little different. One possible explanation is that, in the 450 mm (17·7 in.) furnaces, the coal is kept for a longer period at approximately 100°C, this being the temperature at which oxidation occurs.

VI. CONCLUSIONS

Oxidation of coal before carbonization can only be justified in a small number of cases.

If it is intended to carry out carbonization of the normal type, to produce metallurgical coke, it is almost always more economical to reduce the fluidity of the coal (should it happen to be excessive, which is very rare* by incorporating nonfusible constituents in the mixture (e.g. low-volatile coal, coke dust, semicoke), or even constituents which are both nonfusible and oxidizing (nonfusible coals with a high volatile content, lignites, ferric-oxide powder); these latter additives have an even stronger effect.

Inert constituents of suitable particle size have the additional advantage that they reduce fissuration (by a mechanism independent of any action on the plasticity).

It was in this way that the Lorraine coalfield was able to solve a problem connected with the carbonization of briquettes (Tetralor). To eliminate any deformation of the briquettes during heating, they were made of a mixture—in suitable proportions—of high-volatile coking coal (slightly fusible, with 36% to 38% of volatiles and 9% to 10% of oxygen) and dry high-volatile coal (nonfusible, with 37% to 39% of volatiles and 11% to 12% oxygen).

Preliminary oxidation would, perhaps, be necessary before carrying out semi-carbonization in a fluidized bed, when treating coking coals; but, as we have seen, this is not definitely established as yet.

It seems probable that the most simple and most economical technique for oxidizing coal fines is to heat them to approximately 300°C by means of oxidizing gases in a fluidized bed. This treatment is economical, because preheating is carried out at the same time (this raises the calorific value of the semicarbonization gas) and also, possibly, dedusting (which facilitates the condensation of the tars).

Finally, we have seen that it is possible to dry coals which are very sensitive to oxidation, on an industrial scale, without changing their coking properties.

---

* We do not share the opinion of Gillings and others (12) that too high a fluidity could be the cause of the fissuration of the coke.

REFERENCES

1. HOUILLÈRES DU BASSIN D'AQUITAINE and BEAUGRAND M., Method of improving the quality of fusible coals, Fr. P. 1,088,804 (15 Sept. 1954).
2. Ann. Rep., C.E.R.Ch.A.R. 1952. Paris (1953).
3. BEAUGRAND P., Considerations on the artificial anthracite produced at Carmaux, *Fourth Int. Congr. Industr. Heating*, Paper 24, Group II, Sect. 21, 1952. Paris, *Chaleur et Industrie*, 1953.
4. GEORGES P., Low-temperature carbonization, *Ann. Min., Mém.* **136**, No. 6, 46 (1947).
5. CHEREAU J., Oxidation of a coal in air: studies by thermogravimetric analysis between 100° and 270°, *C.R. Acad. Sci.* **234**, 1165 (1952).
6. CHEREAU J., On an anomaly in isothermal thermogravimetric curves recorded with a coal heated in contact with air. *C.R. Acad. Sci.*, **234**, 1368 (1952).
7. GEORGIADIS C., and GAILLARD G., Researches on the kinetics and mechanism of oxidation of coals, *Chim. et. Industr.*, **70**, 383 (1953).
8. SOULÉ J. L., Process of fissuring in coke, *Fuel*, **34**, 68 (1955).
9. BOYER A. F., The mechanical aspects of carbonization, *BrennstChemie*, **37**, 226, (1956).
10. LOISON R., Influence of drying and storage conditions of coke blends, *Charb. de Fr.*, Note Tech. No. 17 (1953).
11. *Ann Rep.*, C.E.R.Ch.A.R. (1955, in the press).
12. GILLINGS D. W., LAWSON W. and WILLING E. G. J., Relation of coal viscosity and coke strength observed in test oven experiments on blending, *C.R. XXVII int. Congr. Industr. Chem.*, *Brussels*, 1954; **2**, 62 (1955).

DISCUSSION

DR.-ING. GEORG HUCK (*Gesellschaft für Kohlentechnik G.m.b.H., Dortmund-Eving*):

Reference is made in the section of the paper dealing with the nonoxidizing drying of coal that the swelling index of a coal may fall off markedly during storage after drying. This phenomenon interests us greatly, since we have observed a similar subsequent oxidation. Would you explain this fact by a subsequent change in the type of oxygen bond, or do you assume that diffusion of oxygen has taken place?

You have observed that only a small amount of CO_2 is evolved at the beginning of oxidation. According to our experience, the quantity of CO_2 formed during oxidation depends on the type of coal. In the case of younger coals—which can be readily oxidized—CO_2 is equally readily given off; with older coals, on the other hand, both oxidation and CO_2 formation were more difficult.

A little time ago we attempted, in vain, to increase the phenol yield from low-temperature carbonization, by preoxidation of the coal. Have you found—when subjecting oxidized coal to low-temperature carbonization—particular oxygen compounds to be present in the tar or in the liquor? What we have particularly in mind is the fact that acids of low-molecular weight and aldehydes are found in the waste gases from the oxidation of coal.

AUTHOR:

Certainly, oxygen diffuses into the coal through small superficial cracks. Fine-size coal can be considered as almost homogenously oxidized.

I agree with the experiences of Dr. Huck. When dealing with high-rank coals, CO_2 is much more difficult to split off than is the case with low-rank coal.

We made no investigations about the influence of oxidation on the liquid byproducts during carbonization. But I expect the byproducts from these oxidized coals would not be very different from byproducts from coals naturally rich in oxygen.

DR. D. W. GILLINGS (*Imperial Chemical Industries Ltd., Reading*):

I should like to comment on the influence of oxidation of coal on its coking properties, affecting its behaviour in the classical coke-oven process. In presenting his paper, Monsieur Boyer has taken more account of the conditions in which it is possible to obtain an apparent improvement or, at least, a maintenance of coking properties where a coking coal of specified properties is oxidized and blended with other coking coal. I would refer to a number of experiments carried out at the Coal Research Establishment, actually some years ago now, dealing with a high-volatile coal blend with "medium coking" properties indicated by Code No. 502/602. A series of trials was carried out, in which 50% of the charge was oxidized to different oxygen uptake. From these experiments it was found

B

that the shatter index was somewhat increased if there was only a limited oxidation of the oxidized component, but if the oxidation was carried further the shatter index fell off very rapidly. I agree with Monsieur Boyer that the magnitude of these changes was perhaps not very important from the viewpoint of commercial application or the upgrading of coals for commercial and economic use in coke ovens, or of adding to carbonization coal reserves. But there is a point of interest relative to understanding the mechanism of coking, and the important features of the coking process. Monsieur Boyer makes a considerable point, not only in this paper but in other publications which are of very great interest, that the shrinkage coefficient of the coals comprising the blend around the plastic region and the postplastic region is critical in governing the shatter indices of the coke. I think I would agree, and I think most of you who have worked in the field will agree, that the shrinkage coefficients go very far to rationalizing effects observed in many blending experiments. But I think it also relevant to take account of plasticity changes in discussing observations on the very lightly oxidized coals and their behaviour in blends with coking coals—and they are very like lower-rank coals in this respect: it is known that quite substantial quantities of lower rank coals can be blended in good coking blends. It is possible to associate change of coke properties quite closely with the change in plasticity without taking account of changes in shrinkage. We have many instances where plastic behaviour gives an indication of cohesion at the fusion stage, which is of course critical; if there is no cohesion there is no coke formation: slight oxidation appears to assist this cohesion, raising the apparent " viscosity " of the coal, and the $1\frac{1}{2}$-inch shatter index of the coke.

AUTHOR:

Dr. Gillings points out that he has improved the shatter test of coke (that is to say, he has succeeded in reducing the degree of fissuration) by previously oxidizing some of the coal, which was a high-volatile coal. I have not carried out experiments of this kind, but the results do not surprise me. In point of fact, a similar result can be obtained by adding—to the high-volatile coal—a coal with a very high oxygen content, 10% to 12%; it would seem that, very frequently, oxidized coals behave in the same way as do coals which are naturally rich in oxygen.

This diminution of fissuration by means of the addition of coal with a high oxygen content was studied some years ago at Cerchar. It can be very easily explained by referring to the reduction in the rate of contraction of the mixture. This is a difficult phenomenon to explain in a few words, but the general outline of the process is as follows. The oxidized coals (or coals naturally rich in oxygen) have a relatively low rate of contraction in the temperature range from 460°C to 480°C, relative to a heating rate of 2°C/min (see Fig. 3). This is because the thermal decomposition is partially displaced to other temperature zones, such as the ranges between 360°C and 400°C and between 500°C and 600°C. The temperature of solidification of mixtures of coals with a high volatile content is situated precisely in this temperature range of 460°C to 480°C. Thus the average rate of contraction of the mixture at the temperature of solidification is somewhat reduced. I would remind you that we think that this rate is the principal factor which governs the fissuration of the coke and, consequently, the strength as determined by the shatter test.

Side by side with this favourable effect on fissuration, oxidation of a part of the charge has an opposite effect; it reduces the temperature of solidification of the mixture, thus indirectly increasing the maximum rate of contraction.

One or the other of these effects may predominate, according to the proportions of high volatile or oxidized coals in the mixture, and also according to the respective size grading of the two components. More precise explanations can be found in our publications on carbonization (see e.g. A. F. Boyer, *Laboratory Investigation on the Introduction of High-Volatile Coals into Coking Blends*, 1955 Congress of the Technical Association of the Gas Industry in France). Equal proportions and a size grading which is not excessively fine constitute favourable factors. An excessively fine-sized grading and the oxidation of more than 70% of this mixture would, in my opinion, be disadvantageous.

I do not consider that it is possible to explain an improvement in the shatter-test values by the reduction in the plasticity of the coal, for the following reasons:

The various factors which we observed at Verneuil as acting on the quality of the coke have all been capable of explanation by the variations in the rate of contraction.

No explanation of a rational nature has been given—to the best of my knowledge—of the relation between the plasticity of fused coal and the fissuration of coke after its formation. From a mechanical point of view, the two phenomena would appear to be unrelated.

The assessment of the results obtained in the experimental coking plant at Marienau, where hundreds of widely differing mixtures have been carbonized, has not shown a general correlation between the quality of the coke and the plasticity. The correlation does, nevertheless, exist for certain types of blend; I will return to this point later.

In my opinion, the idea of plasticity of a mixture of coals does not correspond to any parameter existing in a coke oven. In such an oven, as Alpern has shown, the particles of coal fuse and become agglomerated without becoming mixed;* each component of the mixture maintains its own plasticity. In a plastometer of the Gieseler type, the fineness of grinding and the mixing produced by the rotation of the blades give, on the contrary, an almost homogeneous mixture of the different fusible coals. The plasticity of this mixture is what we measure.

It is difficult to understand how the quality of the coke could be governed—in a causal relationship—by the properties of a mixed phase which might have been formed, but which does not form in reality.

Notwithstanding this, as Dr. Gillings has very rightly pointed out—and as we have found at Marienau—there is observed in certain cases a statistical correlation between the plasticity and the shatter-test index; this can easily be explained in another way. If we consider a very plastic coal with a high volatile content (30% to 35% for instance), this coal, when used alone, gives a very fissured coke.

There are two methods of reducing this fissuration: either, we can raise its solidification temperature; this would best be done by adding a coal with from 16% to 22% of volatile matter, such coals being generally only slightly plastic, or we can reduce the rate of contraction, by adding inert substances or substances with a low contraction (anthracite, coke, oxidized coal, iron ore).

In either case, one would record a simultaneous reduction of the plasticity and improvement in the shatter test, but the effects on the plasticity and the shatter-test index are completely unrelated. In addition, it is possible to find certain components (e.g. coals with 37% of volatile matter and a swelling index of from 5 to 6) which simultaneously reduce the plasticity and the shatter-test index of a very fusible coal; they thus constitute an exception to the correlation just referred to.

There is, of course, always a minimum value of plasticity, below which the agglutination of particles of coal cannot occur; this phenomenon has nothing whatever to do with fissuration or with contraction.

When I spoke of the slight economic interest of oxidation in the preparation of coke, I did not mean to imply that one cannot by this means attain good results. What I wanted to say was that, generally, it will be advantageous to use coals which are naturally rich in oxygen rather than coals which have been artificially oxidized. The coals with high oxygen content may be in short supply in certain districts, but they are, on the whole, much more abundant than coking coals.

With regard to the effectiveness of such mixtures, I would like to quote the following example: A very fusible coal with 35% of volatile matter and 6% of oxygen, gives a shatter-test index at 40 mm of 50 to 60. By mixing 40% of this coal with 60% of a coal with 40% volatile matter, 12% of oxygen and no coking properties at all (shatter-test index = 0), we obtain for the mixture a shatter-test index of 76 to 80, with certain size gradings.

MR. T. KENNAWAY (*Simon-Carves, Ltd., Stockport*):

I would like to ask Monsieur Boyer one or two questions. In Monsieur Boyer's paper he refers to the Carmonoix process. I wonder if he can say whether any investigations have been made into the actual mechanism which takes place when the pretreatment stage is carried out. I am referring to his statement where he mentions that the coal briquettes are held at elevated temperatures for a number of hours. I ask this because he mentions that they lose 2% by weight, while, further on in the paper, he mentions that coals gain weight when they are oxidized. What I wish to ask is this; is oxidation of the coal taking place here or is it simply a polymerization of the pitch with loss of the more volatile constituents from the pitch?

Another point which might be added to Monsieur Boyer's list, when he mentions the influence of oxidation on coal, is the fact that when coal is oxidized one can produce from it a more reactive coke and that is most important when briquetted fuels are made for domestic use.

Finally, in his conclusions, Monsieur Boyer seems to imply that a similar effect to oxidation can be achieved by blending coals of different types. I am wondering whether he has any evidence, from Gieseler plastometer curves, for instance, to show that by blending coals a similar effect to oxidation of single or blended coals can be obtained. For instance, I know that it is possible to narrow the plastic range by oxidation. Can this also be done by blending?

AUTHOR:

In the Carmonoix process there is simultaneous oxidation of the coal and of the pitch. If the

---

* ALPERN B. The optical anisotropy of coke; its application to the problem of mixtures. **Congress on Coal Science**, Heerlen, 2/3 May 1955.

same experiment is made in an atmosphere of pure nitrogen, there is no modification of the briquette. This proves that oxidation occurs.

There is a decrease of about 2% in the weight of the briquettes during the industrial treatment at 180°C. In laboratory experiments on coal (Fig. 1 and Ref. 5), an increase in weight is recorded in the same conditions; and a temperature of about 250°C is necessary to get a decrease of weight in twelve hours. I do not know the reason for this discrepancy. Perhaps the pitch oxidizes more readily than the coal.

The oxidized coal gives a more reactive coke for domestic use. In some cases we noticed larger BET surfaces for low-temperature cokes if the coal had been oxidized.

If you add a high-oxygen coal or a lignite to a bituminous coal the plastometer records a decrease in plasticity and a reduction of the plastic range almost exactly as when you oxidize the bituminous coal. The best results are obtained if the high oxygen coal is very finely crushed, because the physico-chemical reaction between the two coals is an almost heterogeneous reaction, occurring only in the region of the contact surfaces, at a distance of 0·01 mm to 0·1 mm from this surface.

MR. W. LAWSON (*National Coal Board, Stoke Orchard*):

In the course of some work at this Establishment on blending for improvement of coke, some experiments were carried out in which a portion of the coking blend was oxidized and added back to the parent blend. 50% of the charge to the oven was oxidized to varying degrees of oxidation and then blended with the remainder. The charges to the oven were examined in the Gieseler Plastometer and the results are given in the following table:

	Incipient fusion °C	Fluidity divs/min	Solidification °C	1½-inch Shatter Index
Raw Coal	(367)	1,650	466	78
Blend A	361	140	456	84
Blend B	373	22	455	84
Blend C	388	12	(460)	77
Blend D	392	7	452	71

It is interesting to note that these results confirm the findings of Monsieur Boyer on the influence of oxidation on the fluidity characteristics. The extent of oxidation increases from Blend A to Blend D and it is seen that the temperature of incipient fusion increases significantly, the fluidity drops very rapidly and the solidification point shows hardly any change.

The effect on coke quality, as measured by the 1½-in. shatter index, is to give a maximum strength for Blends A and B. A further increase in the extent of oxidation causes a deterioration in the coke quality. We therefore consider that a controlled oxidation of a portion of the coking blend is worthy of consideration for the improvement of coke quality. It is true, as Monsieur Boyer points out, that the same effect can be obtained by the addition of low-volatile coal or semicoke. Which of these methods is adopted depends on transport costs for the low-volatile coal and the relative processing costs for the production of semicoke and the oxidation of part of the coking blend.

In part, we agree with Monsieur Boyer that the use of oxidized coal does not prevent fissuring. In the example quoted, the percentage of large coke was reduced when part of the charge was oxidized. Thus the percentage retained on the 2-in. screen was reduced from 84·8% to 79·3%. Nevertheless the 1½-in. shatter index of the coke was increased from 78 to 84 and since shatter index is an accepted measure of coke quality, it is reasonable to regard this increase of 6 points as a significant improvement.

AUTHOR:

The answer is about the same as for Dr. Gilling's question. In addition, I can add this point:

There are theoretical reasons for believing that this improvement in the quality by oxidation of one component of the blend is valid only for coke of average quality. If you consider coking blends with solidification point below 480°C (at rate of heating 2°C/min) you can expect that the shrinkage rate in this area will be lowered by oxidation (see Fig. 3). But with high-quality coking blends (solidification point above 490°C), you can no longer expect this improvement, because you are in an area where the shrinkage rate is unchanged or even increased by oxidation (see Fig. 3, above the point where the curves intersect).

DR. W. IDRIS JONES (*Chairman*):

Can I ask you if, when coarsely ground high-volatile weakly caking coals are preoxidized superficially, you find you can introduce a greater proportion of those oxidized coals into the blend, than if they were finely divided?

AUTHOR:

We did not make many experiments at Verneuil on coking of oxidized coals. But, by comparison with coals naturally rich in oxygen, I expect it would be possible to introduce a larger amount of oxidized coals of coarse size (for instance, <3 mm) than of finely divided (<1 mm) sizes.

DR. W. IDRIS JONES (*Chairman*):

We had some experience some years ago when low-volatile coals were used as a blend constituent. The problem was to introduce as high a percentage of these coals into the blend as possible. By finely dividing the strongly caking component and blending with the coarsely divided low-volatile coals we were able to get a blend with a volatile content of less than 18%, to give a first class metallurgical coke. The normal volatile content of the charge blend was about 23% to 24%. So I just wondered if you did find the same thing with the oxidized coarse low-rank grains; apparently you don't.

DR. D. M. L. GRIFFITHS (*National Coal Board, Stoke Orchard*):

I understand that the product from the " Anthracine 54 " process, that is, the process in which pitch-bound briquettes are oxidized to reduce their smoke emission, is harder and stronger than the untreated briquette.

Would Monsieur Boyer confirm this? If so, perhaps he would describe how the strength of the briquettes changes during the oxidation treatment. In experiments here at the Coal Research Establishment we have found that the strength of the briquettes decreases during the first half-hour or so of the treatment but thereafter it increases until the strength equals or surpasses that of the untreated briquettes.

Has Monsieur Boyer any information on how different types of heating affect the time of treatment? From his paper I understand that heat is introduced in the oxidizing gases, but has he used, for example, infra-red heating to raise the temperature of the briquettes?

The process of oxidizing briquettes to make them smokeless on combustion appears to be a very promising process but it is applicable only to briquettes made from coals which are themselves more or less smokeless. Has Monsieur Boyer any information on the use of this method for the higher-volatile-content coals?

We are, of course, interested in this method of treating briquettes, to make them smokeless, particularly as a subsequent treatment of the products from our hot briquetting processes. In this process we have the briquettes leaving the briquetting press at the temperatures required for the oxidation treatment, and since the smoky constituent, that is, the pitch, is present in smaller quantities in these briquettes than when they are made by the conventional process, we should be able to reduce appreciably the time required for the oxidation treatment.

AUTHOR:

I have no information with regard to the increase of strength of the briquette during oxidation. With regard to the heating of the briquettes, the heat is first introduced by hot gases. After this the reaction is exothermic. I have never heard of experiments with infra-red heating. I agree entirely with Dr. Griffiths: the process is applicable only to briquettes made from smokeless coal.

DR. H. A. STANDING (*National Coal Board, Stoke Orchard*):

The kinetics curve in Fig. 1 shows the variation in the increase in weight of the sample with the time of oxidation. Dr. Boyer finds that during the initial stages of oxidation the gain in weight corresponds to the fixation of oxygen, i.e. there is no gasification of the carbon. I should like to ask how much oxygen can be taken up by the coal before water and oxides of carbon are evolved as gaseous oxidation products.

The Arrhenius plot in Fig. 2 gives the energy of activation for the fixation of oxygen by coal in the initial stages of oxidation. The value obtained is 15 kcal/mole. This value is comparable with those quoted by Schmidt for work in which gaseous oxidation products are evolved but is considerably higher than the value of 6 kcal/mole determined by Georgiadis and Gaillard for the fixation of oxygen by the coal. I should be pleased if Dr. Boyer would comment on this.

AUTHOR:

A few analyses have shown that, for an increase in weight of from 1% to 2%, the degree of gasification of carbon was low as compared with fixation of oxygen.

I believe—although I have no direct experimental proof—that if we consider the beginning of the curve of variation in weight by itself (increase in weight of less than 0·5 %, for example) there would be no interference by secondary gasification reactions and only fixation of oxygen would be recorded.

The difference between the values of 6·5 kcal and 15 kcal seems to me to be very difficult to explain. There are probably two successive reactions, fixation of oxygen and gasification of carbon in the form of oxidized products. The second reaction would seem to have an energy of activation which is higher than that of the first reaction, because the second predominates at high temperatures. If we study the overall reaction by measuring the fixed oxygen, we are in fact measuring a difference in rate between the two reactions. This would presumably give us—for the overall reaction—a lower " apparent energy of activation " than that for the primary reaction of fixation of oxygen.

This, therefore, constitutes a difficulty: we should obtain a higher value for the energy of activation for the primary reaction than is the case with the process as a whole, whereas in fact the observed results point to the contrary.

Personally, I have attempted to measure the fixation of oxygen by taking the initial rates. If I now consider the entire process, taking e.g. the rate of increase in weight once 3 % or 4 % of oxygen has been fixed, I find an " energy of activation " which is very ill-defined, but is certainly less than 15 kcal. This appears to me to be quite consistent.

The difference between the results obtained, on the one hand, by Georgiadis and Gaillard, and on the other, by myself, is not attributable alone to the manner of analysing the experimental curves, but also to the curves themselves. It will be seen on reference to the experimental results (Fig. 2 of Georgiadis, Fig. 1 in my paper) that the temperature seems to have less effect on the development of the reaction in the trials made by Georgiadis and Gaillard than was the case with my experiments. I can offer no explanation for this.

MR. S. D. SAVAGE (*National Coal Board, Stoke Orchard*):

During his description of the manufacture of semicoke at Bruay, Monsieur Boyer said that the oxidation treatment of the coal is checked by means of an " index of agglutination ". I assume that this test is the same as the one in use in Great Britain; that is, the coal under test is mixed with definite proportions of sand and carbonized. The coked mass, after cooling, is subjected to a certain load and the proportion of sand to coal in the mass which just supports the load is assumed to be the agglutinating value of the coal.

We have used such a test to determine whether coal has been sufficiently oxidized for the manufacture of carbonized briquettes. However, in a process involving oxidation, briquetting and briquette carbonization, using pitch as the binder in the briquetting stage, the degree of oxidation is sometimes critical. In many cases we have noticed that the agglutinating value alone was not sufficient and that it was necessary to couple this determination with one in which the swelling number of the oxidized coal was also determined.

Has Monsieur Boyer also experienced this or were the conditions of carbonizing the oxidized coals in his work not so critical as when briquettes are carbonized?

AUTHOR:

Yes. This index of agglutination is determined by the percentage of sand in the sample, when it just resists load. It is not at all accurate. It is not necessary in our case to maintain any coking properties, as it would be when manufacturing briquettes. This is much easier. But I agree, this is probably not accurate enough for checking briquetting manufacture.

DR. R. G. PARTINGTON (*National Coal Board, Stoke Orchard*):

It may be of interest to mention, in connection with the subject of the oxidation of coal, that I have recently started an experimental study of the reaction of gaseous sulphur dioxide with coal. At 350°C, there was evidence of an exothermic reaction and of the formation of hydrogen sulphide and sulphur in the products. After reaction with the SO_2, the volatile content, carbon content, and hydrogen content of the coal were lower; this was accompanied by a substantial increase in the sulphur content and a small increase in the oxygen content. The coking properties of the coal were destroyed. This work. which is at present only in its early stages, is being continued.

AUTHOR:

This is very interesting. In a connected field, I read a paper recently which discussed the influence of nitric oxide on carbonization.* There seem to be certain analogies between the actions of oxygen sulphur dioxide, and nitric oxide.

---

* BERKOWITZ and DAMMEYER., *Pyrolysis of coal in the presence of nitric oxide. Fuel*, **35**, 19, (1956).

MR. R. L. BOND (*British Coal Utilisation Research Association, Leatherhead*):

With regard to Monsieur Boyer's Fig. 3, Dr. Napier in the British Coal Utilisation Research Association laboratories has made some calculations based on his own studies of the volatile release from low-rank coals. Values for the activation energies associated with the composite process occurring in the temperature range 320°C to 480°C have been calculated. The value is 40 ± 5 kcal/mole and is similar for the three samples. This suggests that the basic process occurring is the same in each case although the material evolved at the beginning may be slightly modified by oxidation over the temperature range quoted by the author, viz. 360°C to 420°C, for the emission of oxygen-containing material. Now, Georgiadis and Gaillard have shown that the temperature at which the maximum evolution of oxygen-containing material from both unoxidized and oxidized coals occurs is 550°C. Hence it seems that oxidation does not radically alter that part of the differential weight loss curve above 500°C. These observations confirm the view that the oxygen introduced by oxidation is of a superficial nature in that it does not modify the basic structure of the coal.

The overall loss in weight that occurs when a coal is oxidized and subsequently heated to 500°C is the same as the weight loss that occurs on carbonizing an unoxidized coal to the same temperature. This may be shown as follows. It is possible to estimate the weight loss that occurs during oxidation and subsequent heating of the oxidized coal to 300°C from results obtained in the British Coal Utilisation Research Association by Farenden. Adding to this the loss in weight, given in Fig. 3, when the oxidized coals are carbonized, we find that the overall weight loss up to 500°C is the same as that obtained with the raw coal when carbonized to 500°C. In view of these observations and the effect of oxidation on swelling I would be interested if the author would comment on how he views the essential difference between oxidation and carbonization, and carbonization pretreatments.

Secondly I wish to make a small point concerned with low-temperature oxidation of coals. Farenden has studied this quite extensively in the British Coal Utilization Research Association, and finds that the change in weight of a coal sample on oxidation is largely dependent on the oxidation temperature. The change in weight over a given time interval depends upon the quantity of oxygen reacting with the coal and the distribution of this oxygen between the oxidized solid and the oxidation gases—carbon dioxide, carbon monoxide and water vapour—produced. Both these factors are temperature dependent: at higher temperatures both the rate of reaction and the proportion of reacting oxygen that appears in gaseous oxidation products are increased. Fig. A shows the change in weight with time of a high volatile coal oxidized at four temperatures, viz. 110°, 175°, 200°, and 250°C. The marked difference in behaviour between the samples oxidized at 200°C and 250°C is believed to be due to the thermal breakdown of oxygen-containing groups, possibly carboxyl groups, at the higher temperature. It would seem, therefore, that a study of loss in weight during oxidation without a complete analysis of the oxygen balance is rather difficult to interpret.

AUTHOR:

Dr. Napier's value of 40 ± 5 kcal seems to be quite right. On the same sample we obtained by different means (constant temperature experiments) the value of 45 kcal for the activation energy of the pyrolysis process.

We always found, during the pyrolysis, the maximum rate of evolution of oxygen at about the same temperature (± 10°C) as the maximum rate of evolution of volatile matter, a result which is somewhat different from Gaillard's.

About the difference between oxidation and carbonization, and carbonization only: this is of course a difficult question. I think that for a slight oxidation, the chemical pyrolysis processes are not fundamentally modified; but a small increase in the quantity of crosslinks between coal molecules at 350°C to 400°C can markedly reduce plasticity.

I agree with the last point. Only at low temperatures, below 200°C to 250°C—and, in addition, only at the beginning of oxidation—there is a likelihood of a simple relationship between oxidation and change in weight. For this reason I have not tried to comment extensively on these curves.

DR. D. J. E. INGRAM (*University of Southampton; communicated*):

Both Monsieur Boyer and Mr. Bond have referred to the free radicals present in coal and their interaction with oxygen in relation to any possible correlation with the swelling or caking properties. The results on the reversible interaction of oxygen with the carbon surface were quoted as disproving the permanent effect of any such interaction, but no mention was made of the electron resonance measurements on oxidized coals which suggest that such a correlation may well exist.

It may therefore be helpful to summarize these two distinct sets of measurements. The first has to do with the admission of oxygen to chars which have been prepared in vacuo. In this case a striking change in the free radical absorption is obtained,* but of a completely reversible nature with change

---

* INGRAM D. J. E. and TAPLEY J. G., *Chemistry & Industry*, 568 (1955).

of oxygen pressure. This is the effect Monsieur Boyer referred to and can be interpreted as entirely due to a physical interaction between the oxygen and carbon surface.

If, however, electron resonance measurements are made on a series of oxidized coals produced by progressive oxidation of one coal (Ellington High Main; Coal Rank Code 702), a definite and non-reversible change of free-radical concentration is obtained. These measurements are summarized in the accompanying table and the fall of free-radical concentration with increasing oxidation is clearly seen.

TABLE

Variation of Free Radical Concentration with Oxidation

Coal analysis			C = O bonds meg/100 g	Free radical content Unpaired electrons/g
%C	%H	%O		
83·2	5·2	10·6*	—	$7·9 \times 10^{18}$
81·5	5·2	11·4	63	$6·9 \times 10^{18}$
81·0	5·0	12·1	94	$6·9 \times 10^{18}$
78·2	4·3	15·6	135	$6·2 \times 10^{18}$
76·1	4·0	18·1	194	$5·2 \times 10^{18}$
68·3	2·7	27·2	365	$2·5 \times 10^{18}$
66·2	2·3	29·5	550	$2·3 \times 10^{18}$

* Parent coal of series, i.e. unoxidized coal.

It would therefore appear that the presence or absence of the free radical concentration may well be correlated with swelling or caking properties of the coal, and preliminary measurements with sulphur and other compounds appear to support this view.

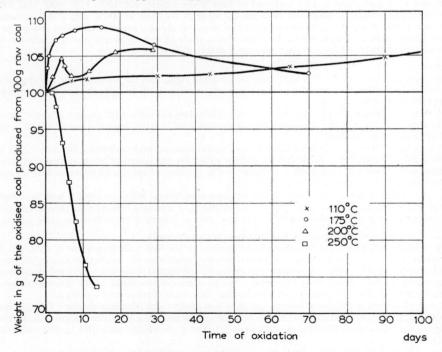

Fig. A. Oxidation of a low rank coal—variation of weight with time.

FLUIDIZED OXIDATION OF COAL

By G. I. JENKINS

Coal Research Establishment, National Coal Board, Great Britain

Summary—The caking and swelling properties of a coal can be destroyed by a mild oxidation. By such oxidation the range of coals suitable for briquette carbonization can be extended. The paper describes a pilot-plant investigation of the oxidation process using the dense-phase fluidization principle. The plant was designed for a normal oxidation capacity of 1 ton per hour, and the heating was carried out in two stages. The preheating vessel enabled the coal to be raised to about 200°C and the reaction vessel completed the heating to temperatures within the range 250°C to 450°C.

The investigations were confined to a coal with a volatile content of approximately 17%. The reaction was exothermic and the heat evolution was proportional to the oxygen consumed from the fluidizing gas. This coal was made suitable for carbonization when the oxygen consumption was about 0·4 s.c.f. per pound of coal. At this degree of oxidation the exothermic heat of reaction was 90 B.t.u./lb. and accounted for almost half of the total heat requirements. For residence times within the range 12 to 40 minutes the oxygen consumption was a function of temperature and independent of time, indicating that the rate of oxidation decreases rapidly with the extent of oxidation. Other process conditions being identical, the rate of oxidation is a linear function of the surface area per unit weight of coal processed. A reduction of coal particle size therefore enables less severe reaction conditions to be employed for a given degree of oxidation.

Résumé—Les propriétés d'agglutination et de gonflement d'un charbon peuvent être détruites par une oxydation modérée. On peut étendre au moyen d'une oxydation de ce genre la gamme des charbons convenant à la carbonisation d'agglomérés. Le mémoire décrit une étude en atelier pilote sur le traitement d'oxydation qui a été faite en appliquant le principe de la fluidisation en phase dense. L'atelier a été conçu pour une capacité normale d'oxydation de 1 t/h et la chauffe se faisait en deux phases. Le récipient de chauffage préalable était susceptible d'élever la température de charbon à environ 200°C et le récipient pour réaction complétait le chauffage à des températures se tenant dans l'intervalle 250° à 450°C.

Les études portèrent seulement sur un charbon ayant une teneur en matières volatiles d'environ 17 %. La réaction était exothermique et le dégagement de chaleur était proportionnel à l'oxygène consommé dans le gaz produisant la fluidisation. Le charbon était rendu apte à la carbonisation lorsque la consommation d'oxygène était d'environ 0,4 pied cube normal par livre de charbon (0,02 m³/kg). Pour ce degré d'oxydation la chaleur exothermique de réaction était de 90 B.t.u./lb. (50 kcal/kg), elle comptait pour environ la moitié de tous les besoins de chaleur. Pour une durée de séjour de 12 à 40 minutes la consommation d'oxygène était fonction de la température et était indépendante du temps, ce qui indique que la vitesse d'oxydation décroît rapidement au fur et à mesure que l'oxydation se développe. Toutes autres conditions de traitement restant identiques, la vitesse d'oxydation est une fonction linéaire de l'aire superficielle par unité de poids du charbon traité. Une réduction de la dimension de particule du charbon permet donc de faire appel à des conditions d'oxydation moins sévères pour obtenir un degré déterminé d'oxydation.

Zusammenfassung—Das Back- und Blähvermögen einer Kohle lässt sich durch leichte Oxydation zerstören. Auf diese Weise kann man den Bereich der Kohlen erweitern, die sich für die Herstellung rauchloser Brennstoffe in Form von Schwelbriketts eignen. In dem Aufsatz wird eine Versuchsanlage beschrieben, die der Erforschung der Oxydation von Kohle im Wirbelbett dienen sollte. Sie war für eine Durchsatzleistung von 1 t/h ausgelegt, die Erhitzung erfolgte in zwei Stufen. In einem Vorerhitzer wurde die Kohle auf eine Temperatur von etwa 200°C gebracht. Im Reaktionsgefäss erfolgte dann eine Steigerung auf Temperaturen zwischen 250° und 450°C. Die Untersuchungen beschränkten sich auf eine Kohle mit etwa 17% flüchtigen Bestandteilen. Die Reaktion verlief exothermisch, und die Entwicklung von Wärme war dem Verbrauch an Sauerstoff aus dem Trägergas proportional. Die Kohle wurde für die Schwelung brauchbar, wenn der Sauerstoffverbrauch rd. 0,4 Kubikfuss je Pfund Kohle betrug (0,02 m³/kg). Bei diesem Oxydationsgrad wurden durch die Reaktion 90 B.t.u./lb. (rd. 50 kcal/kg) frei, was etwa die Hälfte des Gesamtwärmebedarfs deckt. Bei Verweilzeiten zwischen 12 und 40 min war der Sauerstoffverbrauch abhängig von der Temperatur, jedoch unabhängig von der Zeit. Hieraus geht hervor, dass die Oxydationsgeschwindigkeit mit

zunehmender Oxydierung rasch nachlässt. Bei sonst gleichen Voraussetzungen ist die Oxydationsgeschwindigkeit eine lineare Funktion der spezifischen Oberfläche der zu behandelnden Kohle.
Bei feinerer Aufmahlung der Kohle lässt sich also ein bestimmter Oxydationsgrad unter weniger
scharfen Reaktionsbedingungen erreichen.

The National Coal Board are already large-scale producers of solid smokeless fuel
at their coke ovens and by the manufacture of "Phurnacite".[1] The capacity of
the South-Wales "Phurnacite" plant is being doubled. This will make available
a further 300,000 tons (300,000,000 kg) per annum of a smokeless fuel which is of
exceptionally high quality for domestic boilers and closed stoves. This fuel is made
by briquetting a pitch-coal mixture and carbonizing the resulting briquettes. Further
extensions of "Phurnacite" production may prove difficult since the supply of suitable coal is limited. The preferred coal for this process is a noncaking coal of about
12% volatile content. It is essential that the coal used should be noncaking and
nonswelling, otherwise the briquettes will distort and stick together in the carbonizing
oven. This criterion precludes the use of coals of slightly higher volatile content
since, although otherwise suitable, they have too high a caking index. In order to
extend the range of suitable coals it is necessary to destroy the caking properties
before subjecting them to briquetting and oven carbonization.

It is well known that a mild oxidation will reduce the caking and swelling properties of a coal. The coal which is used for the briquetting process is of small particle size. Hence, since the oxidation process consists in raising the temperature of a
finely divided solid and contacting it with a gas containing oxygen, it was considered
that fluidization would be the ideal method of carrying out the reaction. Preliminary
experiments, using a reaction vessel of 4-in. (10·2 cm) diameter, showed that this was
the case. By the addition of small amounts of oxygen to the coal, it was possible to
produce a product which gave pitch-bound briquettes which were nonsticking and
nonswelling when carbonized under standard conditions. The amount of oxidation
required varies with the properties of the original coal. In general, the required
degree of oxidation could be obtained by employing temperatures between 250°C
and 450°C and coal residence times between 20 minutes and 3 minutes.

Sufficient data were obtained from the operation of the small fluidized unit to
enable a larger pilot plant to be designed and erected. The most convenient method
of raising the temperature of the coal is to use hot gas for the fluidization, but this
method introduced a problem. On account of the fine particle size of the coal, the
amount of gas which could be introduced was limited to an amount corresponding
to a linear velocity in the vessel of about 1 ft. per second (30 cm/sec). Velocities in
excess of this led to an excessive load on the cyclone recovery system.

With this limitation it follows that for a coal feed rate of 1 ton per hour (1000 kg/hr)
in a vessel of 2 ft. (61 cm) diameter, the temperature of the fluidizing gas would have
to be in excess of 2000°C in order to enable the coal to reach 400°C. Such high
temperatures would cause obvious difficulties. If, for the same conditions, the vessel
diameter were increased to 4 ft. (122 cm) than a gas temperature of 1000°C could be
employed. Since the contact time for oxidation is of the order of minutes, the
diameter/height ratio would be very large if fluidizing gas temperatures in excess of
1000°C are to be avoided. This would lead to difficulties with gas distribution if
good fluidization were to be maintained. These considerations ignore the heat

evolution or absorption of the oxidation reaction. The reaction is, in fact, exothermic [2, 3, 4] but its magnitude for the particular coals to be studied was not known. Since the plant was a pilot unit, it was decided to base the design on a zero heat of reaction.

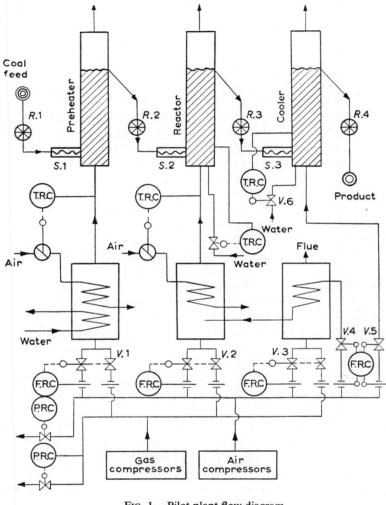

FIG. 1.—Pilot plant flow diagram
PRC=Pressure Recorder/Controller
FRC=Flow Recorder/Controller
TRC=Temperature Recorder/Controller.

In order to avoid vessels of excessive diameter, the heating was carried out in two stages. The first vessel was designed to enable the coal temperature to be raised to about 200°C and the second vessel designed to complete the heating to temperatures within the range 250°C to 450°C. The flow diagram of the larger pilot unit is shown in Fig. 1. The design basis was for a nominal oxidation capacity of 1 ton per hour (1000 kg/hr). The preheating reaction and cooling vessels operate on the fluidized bed principle. Dry, fine coal is continuously fed through the rotary gas-sealing valve, $R1$, and the screw feeder, $S1$, into the preheater column, which is 2 ft. (61 cm) diameter, where its temperature is raised to the desired value. The heated coal overflows through a side off-take pipe into the reactor, also of 2 ft. (61 cm) diameter, via the rotary valve $R2$ and the screw feeder $S2$. In the reactor the fluidizing gas is a mixture of combustion gas and air. The oxidation product is cooled to a safe storage temperature in the final vessel by fluidizing with air and directly injecting water into the bed. The quantity of air used in the cooling vessel is such that the partial pressure of the water vapour in the total exit gas is below the saturation pressure at the operating temperature. This method of cooling enabled the product temperature to be lowered to about 80°C and yet maintained it essentially dry. Hot inert gas for preheating is obtained by the combustion of town's gas in a horizontal combustion chamber. Hot oxygen-containing gas is obtained by mixing inert gas, from a similar combustion chamber, with air which is preheated in an indirect heater. The correct air/gas ratio at the burners is achieved by the tandem valves $V1$, $V2$, and $V3$ (Fig. 1). The flow of gas and air are maintained at the preset values by the flow recorder controllers.

As will be seen from the flow diagram, the plant is fully instrumented. It is controlled from a central control panel. The comprehensive automatic control and the recording system enable accurate data to be obtained. The control of the reactor temperature is of interest since two temperature controllers are used. The first temperature controller maintains the fluidizing gas at a temperature slightly in excess of that required. The second temperature controller maintains the desired reaction temperature by the introduction of water into the fluidized bed. This system enables the temperature to be controlled within very close limits and avoids the difficulties due to the lag arising from the large mass of refractory in the transfer line from the combustion chamber and in the base of the reactor. The oxidation reaction proved to be exothermic. Consequently, it was necessary to obtain rapid correction of any rise in the reactor temperature since otherwise the rise in temperature caused an increase in the oxidation rate with a corresponding additional evolution of heat. The use of water injection obviated the difficulty.

The pilot oxidation plant has been operated for long periods and over a wide range of temperature and coal residence times. So far, the investigations have been confined to coal with a volatile content of approximately 17%. On the scale of about 1 ton/hr (1000 kg/hr) it has been established that this coal may be rendered suitable for the manufacture of carbonized briquettes. The process is simple to operate, amenable to automatic control and is not critical with respect to operating variables. Particular attention has been paid to the heat balance and the oxygen requirements since these are of prime importance in the design of commercial oxidation units.

As was to be expected, the heat evolved during the reaction varied with the amount of oxygen consumed from the fluidizing gas. The data obtained for heat evolved versus oxygen consumption, as s.c.f. per pound of coal processed, is given in Fig. 2. Although the temperature and residence times for the individual points varied widely, there is a linear relation between the exothermic heat and the oxygen consumption. The relation is quantitatively very similar to that previously obtained for lower temperatures of oxidation. [2, 3, 4] The oxygen consumption required to render the coal suitable for carbonization is not very critical. The optimum value for the particular sample used is about 0·4 s.c.f. per pound (0·024 Nm³/kg) of coal. At this degree of oxidation the exothermic heat is 90 B.t.U./lb. (50 kcal/kg) and this accounts for

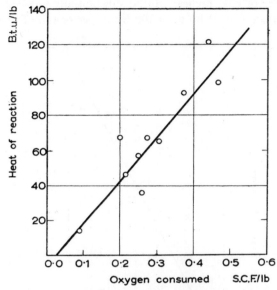

FIG. 2.—Relation between oxidation and heat evolution.

almost half of the total heat requirements. For this coal it is therefore possible to dispense with a preheater and to feed the coal directly to the reactor. The plant has been operated under such conditions.

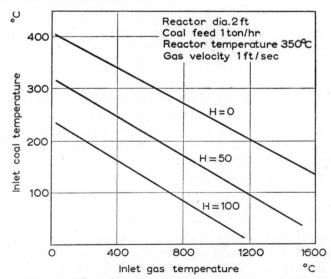

FIG. 3.—Effect of heat of reaction on operating conditions.

The effect of the exothermic heat of oxidation on the heat requirements is shown in Fig. 3, the process conditions being related to those employed in the pilot plant. The three lines refer to heats of oxidation of zero, 50 and 100 B.t.u. per pound (0, 28 and 56 kcal/kg) of coal, respectively. The temperature of the inlet gas to the reactor or the degree of coal preheat can be substantially reduced when the heat of oxidation is in the region of 50 B.t.u. to 100 B.t.u. per pound (28 to 56 kcal/kg).

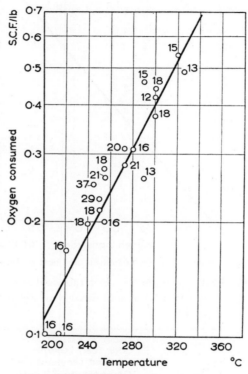

FIG. 4.—Effect of temperature on oxidation.

For residence times within the range 12 min to 40 min the oxygen consumption is a function of temperature and independent of time, as shown in Fig. 4, where the numerical subscripts represent the times of reaction. This confirms previous work at lower temperatures,[2, 3, 4] that the rate of oxidation decreases rapidly with the extent of oxidation. This factor is receiving further detailed investigation since it has an important bearing on the economics of the process.

Since the rate of oxidation increases rapidly with temperature it is desirable, with respect to plant capacity, to operate at as high a temperature as possible. The trend of the present work is towards the use of temperatures above those at which thermal decomposition is normally regarded as taking place. It has been found, for the particular coals studied, that thermal decomposition is not serious at the very short contact times required for oxidation at the high temperatures.

Another factor which has a bearing on the rate of oxidation is the particle size of the coal which is being processed. A coal, of 17% volatile content, was ground to three different particle size distributions and oxidized in the pilot plant, all other process conditions, including contact time, being identical. The oxygen consumption,

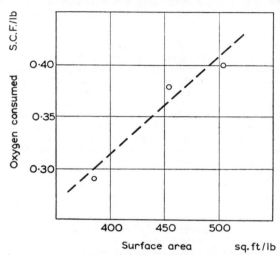

FIG. 5.—Effect of particle size on oxidation rate.

per pound of coal, is given as a function of the surface area per unit weight of coal in Fig. 5. Although there are insufficient data to establish firmly the relation, it is clear that a reduction of particle size enables less severe reaction conditions to be employed for a given degree of oxidation.

REFERENCES

1. Anon., *Coke & Gas* **14**, 5 (1952).
2. WINMILL T. F., *Trans. Instn. Min. Engrs.* **48**, 508 (1914–15).
3. GRAHAM J. I., *ibid.*, **49**, 35 (1914–15).
4. THOMAS W. M., JONES T. D., and GRAHAM J. I., *Proc. S. Wales Inst. Engrs.* **49**, 201, 305 (1933).

DISCUSSION

DR.-ING. GEORG HUCK (*Gesellschaft für Kohlentechnik m.b.H., Dortmund-Eving*):

We have been working for a number of years on the oxidation of hard coals in a fluidized bed. However, our objective is to oxidize the coal beyond the stage necessary to produce a reduction in the caking capacity. Our efforts to do this are governed by a desire to avoid increasing the temperature beyond 250°C. We have been able to establish that the temperature at which the coal attains maximum weight generally lies below 250°C. In addition, a greater degree of decomposition readily occurs at higher temperatures.

Our tests have also proved the value of water injection, although we recorded a higher heat of reaction, generally more than 200 kcal/kg (360 B.t.u./lb.). The supply of cold air can also, in certain conditions, serve to control bed temperature. The coals used in our tests had volatile contents ranging from 7% to 36%. We found that, with these coals, the oxygen concentration in the air had very little effect on the oxidation.

We would like to put the following questions to you regarding your paper:

1. What percentage of the coal is decomposed at temperatures round about 400°C, and how much carbon is lost in the form of CO_2?
2. Could the waste gases from the reaction vessel not be used for preheating the fresh coal?
3. What was the length of time which elapsed between grinding and oxidation? The shorter this period, the greater must be the " oxidizability ".
4. What is the depth of penetration of the oxygen into the coal in your experiments? We were able to record, in general, a depth of penetration of not more than approximately 100μ.

AUTHOR:

Dr. Huck's comments on the use of cold air to control the bed temperature are very interesting. Although we found water injection gave good temperature control on our pilot plant, it has the disadvantage of causing condensation in the exit lines if an excessive quantity has to be used. This condensation can lead to troublesome blockages by the slurry formed from the condensate and the inevitable carry-over of fine coal particles. Such difficulty would be avoided by using air instead of water for temperature control.

With regard to the four questions put by Dr. Huck, I would reply as follows:—

1. I agree that at temperatures round about 400°C carbonization, or decomposition of the coal can take place slowly. However, at these elevated temperatures oxidation is very rapid so that a very short contact time is required to produce the degree of oxidation required to make the coal suitable for briquette manufacture. Over this short time the extent of carbonization was found to be negligible.

   The amount of carbon lost in the form of CO_2 varies according to the oxidizing conditions. At about 400°C we have found that between 0·5% and 1·0% of the carbon in the coal appears as CO_2 in the exit gas from the oxidation vessel.
2. The waste gases from the reaction vessel can be used for preheating the fresh coal and such a heat recovery system has been incorporated in one of our designs for a large-scale plant. Heat recovery was not incorporated in the pilot plant described in this paper since it was considered that such complications would have rendered the process data less accurate and would have added to the difficulty of operation of the plant.
3. The grinding equipment was an integral part of the pilot oxidation plant. Coal of the desired particle size was fed directly from the mill into the preheater without any intermediate storage. The average residence time in the preheating vessel was only about 15 minutes and from this vessel the coal was passed directly into the oxidation vessel. I agree with Dr. Huck that a short period between grinding and reaction leaves a more reactive surface.
4. I regret that I have no information on the depth of penetration of the oxygen into the coal.

MONSIEUR P. FOCH (*Centre d'Etudes et Recherches des Charbonnages de France, Marienau*):

I would like to put a simple question to Dr. Jenkins. He has just described the conditions in which it is necessary to work to obtain a desired degree of oxidation. The question is this: How do you know that you have obtained a desired degree of oxidation? Have you a laboratory test for this purpose, or is it necessary to carry out an industrial or large-scale test to determine this?

AUTHOR:

How to determine the exact degree to which the coal is oxidized is quite a problem. The coal oxidized in this process was required for making briquettes which did not swell and which did not stick when they were carbonized, and which were strong enough to be marketable. The real test, of course, is to carry out a semiscale test. It is costly and time-consuming to do so on a large scale. Consequently, laboratory tests are carried out, using small 1-inch cylindrical briquettes made as nearly as possible under the same conditions as will be used in the full-scale processing. These trial briquettes are placed in laboratory ovens and carbonized at the rate of temperature rise which is about that obtaining at the wall of a vertical chamber. The test briquettes are then examined for swelling, distortion and sticking and for strength. Since a number of semiscale carbonization trials and a number of laboratory tests have been done on the same coal, a rough correlation between the laboratory and the semiscale has been established. But I would not say that the laboratory test can replace the semiscale test. Tests of the agglutinating value and the swelling number are, of course, carried out. Working with one particular coal, and with a background of the laboratory carbonizing test and the semiscale oven test, the agglutinating values and the swelling number can be used to control the operation of the oxidation plant.

DR.-ING. GEORG HUCK (*Gesellschaft für Kohlentechnik m.b.H., Dortmund-Eving*):

In our tests we generally determine the oxidation efficiency by means of the calorific value of coals.

DR. W. IDRIS JONES (*National Coal Board, London*) (*Chairman*):
What is the relation between the change in the calorific value and the oxidation efficiency?

DR.-ING. GEORG HUCK (*Gesellschaft für Kohlentechnik m.b.H., Dortmund-Eving*):
We estimate about 1% per hundred calories. That is sufficient for our purpose.

DR.-ING. W. HERBERT (*Lurgi Gesellschaft für Warmetechnik, Frankfurt-am-Main*):
What is the loss in calorific value through the oxidation of this coal? What is the analysis of the exit gas from the oxidation apparatus? What are the costs for oxidizing 1 ton of this coal?

AUTHOR:
The decrease in calorific value of the coal, at average levels of oxidation, was about 200 B.t.u./lb., but this decrease was slightly offset by a small increase in weight on oxidation.

The analysis of the exit gas varied, of course, with the oxidation conditions. At a reaction temperature of 300°C a typical analysis was carbon dioxide 4·5%, carbon monoxide 0·5%, oxygen 8% and nitrogen 87%. The relatively high oxygen figure arises from the necessity of maintaining a good fluidizing velocity under conditions of low heat-input requirements.

With regard to the costs of oxidation, some preliminary calculations have, of course, been made; I do not think, however, that the figures are sufficiently accurate for results on the scale of the pilot plant of 1 ton per hour to be reliable. I must therefore ask to be excused from giving the costs of oxidation on the basis of the 1 ton per hour plant.

MONSIEUR P. LEDENT (*Institut National de l'Industrie Charbonnière, Liége*):
I would like to ask Dr. Jenkins what is the maximum size of coal which has been treated by fluidized oxidation? The oxidation being probably a superficial effect, I presume there is a maximum size above which fluidized oxidation is not effective as an industrial process to destroy the coking properties of the coal? Is it possible, at the present stage of experiments, to assess what minimum temperature is necessary to carry out fluidized oxidation without external heating and without pre-heating either the coal or the air?

AUTHOR:
The size distribution of the coal which was processed in the pilot oxidation plant was governed by the size requirements for making satisfactory briquettes. Consequently, the size distribution of coal used in all the pilot-plant work was about the same, and practically none of the coal was larger than 30 mesh. Hence, I regret that no information is available regarding the maximum size which can be oxidized by this process. I agree with Monsieur Ledent that the oxidation process is a superficial effect and that this places a limit on the size which can be effectively oxidized.

DR. W. IDRIS JONES (*National Coal Board, London*) (*Chairman*):
Would you not say that, broadly speaking, beyond a size in excess of 30 BS there was a very marked increase in the length of time required for oxidation?

AUTHOR:
That is quite correct. In some experiments on the four-inch oxidizer, which handled about 100 lb. an hour a particle size variable was investigated. The test used was the agglutinating value, which was taken as the index of the amount of reaction which had taken place. When the amount of coal above 10 mesh was considerable the agglutinating value fell but little when the coal was oxidized. But, of course, we have to remember with regard to the agglutinating value test that coal is ground to 72 mesh. Now, it is almost certain that the oxidation reaction is a surface reaction and when the coal is ground to do the agglutinating test fresh surfaces which are not oxidized are exposed.

Monsieur Ledent's second question, the minimum temperature at which the process is self-sustaining with regard to heat, is a very interesting one. To make the reaction self-sustaining at a particular temperature, obviously, there must be sufficient heat of reaction available to raise the incoming coal to that temperature. Whether the reaction will be self-sustaining or not depends, as is shown in Fig. 2 of my paper, on how much oxygen is necessary, or what degree of oxidation is necessary, to render the coal suitable for making carbonized briquettes. For example, if 120 B.t.u./lb. is required to raise the incoming coal to the required temperature, then it is necessary to react 0·5 standard cubic feet of oxygen per lb. of coal. If that happens to be the amount of oxidation needed to make the coal suitable for carbonized briquette manufacture then, of course, no external heat is required. But if the reaction of 0·5 s.c.f./lb. of oxygen gives a coal which is over-oxidized then, although the process requires no external heat, it is of no value since it produces a product which is unsatisfactory for the subsequent processing. The minimum temperature for zero external heat requirement is, therefore, dependent on the degree of oxidation required.

C

MR. T. KENNAWAY (*Simon-Carves Ltd., Stockport*):

Reference is made in Dr. Jenkin's paper to residence times in the fluidized oxidizer of up to 40 minutes, which seems to be relatively long. Similar residence times were quoted in Monsieur Boyer's paper. It may, therefore, be of interest to compare these with the residence time of only a few seconds in a very simple type of oxidizer which has been developed by the National Fuels Corporation of America.

Briefly, this oxidizer and cooler operate as follows:—

Coal which has been previously dried to about 1% surface moisture and is less than $\frac{1}{2}$ mm in size is entrained in an air stream by means of a Fuller-Kinyon pump. This is not fluidization in the sense of fluidization in a fluidized bed, it is entrainment. The entrained coal is then fed into a pipe coil set in a heating furnace, the oxygen for oxidation being supplied by the air stream used to entrain the finely ground coal. The degree of oxidation is controlled by the outlet temperature of the oxidizer and the air stream bearing the coal particles is rapidly cooled in a cooling coil immediately after leaving the oxidizer. The cool oxidized coal is separated from the air stream by means of conventional cyclone and filter equipment.

By running the outlet temperature of the oxidizer in the range 250°C to 475°C most coking coals can be treated. As mentioned, the reaction time is only a few seconds and due to this short contact time, no sticking in the heating coil occurs although the coal is actually heated within the plastic range.

The notable features of this oxidizer are its simplicity of operation and the close control of temperature which can be achieved, the outlet temperature being held at $\pm 2°C$.

A 100 tons-per-day oxidizer of this type has been operated successfully on a pilot plant in the United States and, more recently, a 1-ton-per-hour plant has been built and is operating in this country.

There is one question I would like to ask Dr. Jenkins: We have found that the moisture does effect the oxidation rate quite appreciably; that is why it is dried. I notice in his oxidizer, he admits water on purpose. I am wondering if he has found any similar effect on the oxidation rate and if so, has any difficulty in control resulted?

AUTHOR:

The coal oxidation system developed by the National Fuels Corporation and described by Mr. Kennaway is very interesting. Mr. Kennaway says that it is a very simple type of oxidizer consisting essentially of a dilute-phase coil reactor. Similarly, one can describe the fluidized oxidation system as a simple one, consisting essentially of a dense-phase fluidized-bed reactor. But one must remember that around each reaction system there are ancillaries such as pumps, heaters, coolers, cyclones, etc. Further the oxidation section, whether it be coil or fluidized bed, must have the usual elevators, bunkers, crushers, grinders, etc.

There are advantages and disadvantages in both systems. The NFC system has temperature as the only operating variable. The length of your coil cannot easily be changed if a change of coal should require a change of contact time. The fluidized bed system uses both temperature and contact time, since, of course, the bed height can easily be varied either by a series of off-takes or by a bottom withdrawal through a slide valve and a conventional transport line. The NFC system has a very definite advantage, that of using one pump only for moving the coal, and that pump operates at substantially atmospheric temperature. The reactor and cooler feeding system on the fluidized-bed plant must work at a high temperature, at about the reaction temperature. The high temperature, together with the very fine coal, can cause mechanical difficulties. In the fluidized-bed system mild steel can be used throughout as the material of construction, whereas I am almost sure that the coil in the NFC system has to be of a special alloy steel. Again, with the high velocity transport of the coal (it takes only three seconds to go through the coil) erosion could be a problem. In the fluidized-bed system there is no velocity greater than about 1 ft./sec.

The relative merits depend, in my opinion, on the economics of the process and the ease of operation. Further experience with the two systems on a larger scale will probably be necessary before judgement can be given.

Mr. Kennaway says that the coil system needs a contact time of only three seconds. I am sure Mr. Kennaway would agree that, for the same operating temperature, the same contact time is required in the coil and in the fluidized bed in order to achieve the same degree of oxidation. The coal in which we are interested, one with a volatile content of 17%, required substantial oxidation to destroy its caking properties, a totally different degree of oxidation to what is necessary with coals of say, 30% to 40% volatile content. This was confirmed by the test which was carried out on the coil system by the NFC in the USA. With such coals which are very difficult to oxidize, it is preferable to have the two variables, namely temperature and contact time, rather than just the temperature. If the coal is difficult to oxidize, then with a short contact time, say 3 seconds, it is necessary to employ very high temperatures, perhaps higher than 500°C. In this case, the nature of the oxidation could be quite different to that which was carried out at temperatures of 250°C to 350°C. It must be realised that the oxidized coal is used for making carbonized briquettes and the ultimate criterion is not how the oxidation proceeds, but how good are the final carbonized briquettes.

MR. T. KENNAWAY (*Simon-Carves Ltd., Stockport*):

Dr. Jenkins appears to have been misinformed regarding the details and operation of the NFC Oxidizer and I should like to clarify things a little.

With regard to materials of construction, the coil in the oxidizer we have at the moment is made of FDP stainless steel. But I feel it might be possible to use mild steel. In any case, one would not regard stainless steel of this type as unusual nowadays in chemical engineering practice.

Furthermore, we have not experienced erosion in this coil; that may surprise you, but it is a fact. Whether this is due to the way in which air cushions the effect of the friction between the coal and the coil we do not know, but we do not get erosion. We have had this 1-ton-per-hour oxidizer operating for nearly two years and the only sign of erosion on the oxidizing coil is at the outlet bend, which is very sharp. We feel sure this difficulty can easily be eliminated in any future design by giving the bend a larger radius.

Refering to the slide which was shown by Dr. Jenkins, the NFC Oxidizer is almost literally what you see there in the line diagram. There is very little ancillary equipment and I think you will agree that it is simpler than the fluidized-bed type. In the tests by the NFC to which Dr. Jenkins is referring there was no difficulty in oxidizing the coals.

My recollection is that certain coals were sent which were practically nonswelling; they had a swelling number of about 1 and the NFC process was never intended to deal with that type of coal. It is designed to deal with coals which have a swelling number of 2 or 3 at the least, so that some residual coking power can be left in the briquettes.

Dr. Jenkins says that the true test is: Can good briquettes be made in the end? The answer is: Yes, we can make good carbonized briquettes by this process.

As far as being able to vary both residence time and temperature are concerned, perhaps Dr. Jenkins is right in saying it may be better to have two variables; but as far as I know this has not been necessary with the NFC oxidiser, since so far we have managed to use temperature alone. It may be, that from a practical standpoint, these variables produce an effect on oxidation in a fluidized bed which is different to that in an entrained coal stream.

(Communicated):

With reference to the tests on coals carried out by the National Fuels Corporation, to which Dr. Jenkins referred, I have now consulted our records on this matter and find that five of the six coals sent for tests had, as I stated, a swelling number of 1 and did not give, as could have been predicted, promising test results. From the sixth (swelling number $7\frac{1}{2}$), excellent carbonized briquettes were made and this coal would have proved very suitable as a raw material for the NFC process.

AUTHOR:

In reply to Mr. Kennaway I would first like to say that what I said is no criticism of the NFC process. The point I made about the two variables is that we know so little about the finer details of the process that it is desirable to have control over both temperature and contact time until we are quite happy as to what type of oxidation would make the best briquettes. Further, I did not intend to give the impression that it was difficult to oxidize this particular coal by the NFC process. There is no real difficulty, but a considerable amount of oxygen has to be added to reduce the caking properties to make suitable briquettes, and the point I wish to make clear is that it may necessitate a temperature so high that the type of oxidation would be radically different with the consequent adverse effect, or possible adverse effect, on the final carbonized briquettes.

On the question of erosion I agree with Mr. Kennaway that it is surprising that there is none, except at the outlet bend. The question of replacing the alloy steel coil by one made of mild steel must be considered along with the question of erosion. I wonder if the FDP coil were replaced by a mild steel one whether the erosion would be as small as it is now.

I am sorry, there is one question by Mr. Kennaway which I omitted to answer, that is the effect of moisture on the rate of oxidation. The pilot plant was operated under the two conditions of control. In the first, the inlet gas temperature was controlled and in the second system the gas was at a higher temperature than necessary and water was injected. No difference was found in the rate of oxidation whether water was used or not. That was the case for the low volatile coals. I do not know whether this applies for the high volatile coals. I would not be surprised to find a difference in the effect of the moisture content of the fluidizing gas according to the volatile content of the coal.

MONSIEUR A. F. BOYER (*Centre d'Etudes et Recherches des Charbonnages de France, Verneuil*):
A residence time of ten minutes is quoted in the paper. At Cerchar we have great difficulty in measuring these residence times. How do you determine these times?

AUTHOR:
In answer to Monsieur Boyer, I would first define what I meant by a residence time. It is the time calculated from the weight of coal which is fed to the system per hour and the weight of coal in the fluidized bed. An overflow system was used and the height of the bed was assumed to be at the tip of the overflow pipe. This gave a measure of the bed volume, and knowing the bed density the weight of coal in the reactor could be calculated. The weight of coal going in was obtained from a calibrated feed table. From these data the residence time, or average residence time was calculated. This average residence time gives no information on the true residence time of the different-size particles.

MONSIEUR A. F. BOYER (*Centre d'Etudes et Recherches des Charbonnages de France, Verneuil*):
We went to work in the same manner at Verneuil. The results are not accurate, by reason of errors in the measurements of the volume and density of the fluidized bed. But we were unable to obtain better results.
The measurements of true residence time—which were made by replacing the coal, for a few instants, by a different substance of equivalent density—showed that the residence time for certain particles could be very markedly different from the calculated average. Some particles passed through the apparatus in a few seconds.

AUTHOR:
The density of the fluidized bed was measured by the pressure drop across two points at a known distance apart, using an air-purge system and a differential pressure cell. The system was adjusted to zero with the air flow on the purges, and the purge rates were kept at a constant value.

MR. N. H. WILLIAMS (*Humphreys & Glasgow, Ltd., London*):
I would like to return to the question of particle size, about which quite a bit has been said already, from the point of view that there is nothing absolute about the size of particle required to make a briquette suitable for carbonization; as has already been said today, the proof of the pudding is in the eating. In the preparatory work which was done for the Phurnacite plant, a good deal of pilot work was done on carbonizing in an internally-heated plant by a flow of hot gases. For this work the coal which was used came directly from the washery, and apart from drying, it was not prepared in any way for making the briquettes. Any preparation it received was purely from the point of view of being able to make a briquette of sufficiently sound characteristics. It went through a mixing device in the briquetting plant. Now, when the larger plant was built, where the coking plants were of the oven type, it was found that coal of such a coarse size would not give satisfactory carbonizable briquettes. When considering an installation for dealing with coal which has to be oxidized (that at Aberdare had not to be oxidized) you have to consider the whole installation; in other words, you have to consider the oxidizing plant in conjunction with the carbonizing plant, and it may very well be that with one type of carbonizing plant you would be forced to grind the coal much more finely than with another. So I think that some more work on the effect of size would be of value. In answering an earlier speaker, Dr. Jenkins did mention that they had done some work on the effect of size, but the test which they had used is rather invalidated from the practical point of view because the coal was ground for testing after it had been oxidized. Now if you were making a briquette from coal of that size, you would not grind it up after oxidizing; you would use it at that size, so I think it would be highly interesting to know what is the effect of coal size from the point of view of the oxidizing process.

AUTHOR:
I agree with Mr. Williams that it would be extremely interesting to carry out further experiments to determine the effect of coal size on the oxidation process. The reason why we have not done extensive work on that subject is that the coal size specification for making good green briquettes, which would give a satisfactory carbonized product, was known from previous experience. I do not know how far one could go in changing the particle size distribution and adjusting the degree of oxidation, but it would be an interesting subject for study.

DR. W. IDRIS JONES (*National Coal Board, London*) (*Chairman*):
I think the result might be different in the case of a coal which had initial agglutinating properties, in contrast with the dry steam coals used in the original Phurnacite experiments, which had no agglutinating properties. Any residual agglutination in caking coal after oxidation might have an

effect on the properties of the briquette and on the processing of it. But I agree that here is a question which is worth examining.

MR. HENLEY PRICE (*National Coal Board, Dover*):

The chief question which I wished to ask, namely the capital cost of fluidized bed apparatus for coal oxidation, has already been covered by another contributor. I will therefore only say that it would have been of great interest of Dr. Jenkins had been able to give the Conference some idea of the capital cost of the equipment in terms of rate of oxidation. The addition of a small quantity of oxygen to coal is an easy reaction, and, although the need for conducting it in a controlled manner necessarily adds to the complexity of the plant, the plant described by Dr. Jenkins would appear to be extremely expensive in terms of oxygen added, both in capital and running costs.

With this aspect in mind I would ask Dr. Jenkins if he has considered making use of the principle of the air-slide conveyor for this purpose. A little preparatory work was done on this in my laboratories a year or two ago, but it was not followed up because our interest in the problem receded. However, enough was done to indicate that the principle lends itself readily to this process. Temperature and residence time are easily controlled, and gas flow can be kept low enough to avoid the entrainment of any but the smallest size fractions of the solid phase. Moreover, the apparatus required is simple and inexpensive and it has the great advantage that there are no moving parts in the hot zone.

AUTHOR:

I would agree wholeheartedly with Mr. Price, and I am sure there are others here who would also agree, that a system which minimizes the dustiness of fluidized plant is well worth considering. With regard to the question of the air-slide conveyor, it is true that you get good control of the contact time. I presume—though I am not very familiar with the details of the process—you also get good control of the temperature. If these two conditions can be met, then the system is well worth considering.

MR. R. L. BOND (*British Coal Utilization Research Association, Leatherhead*):

I would like to refer to the question asked this morning of Monsieur Boyer: What is the fundamental mechanism of the oxidation of coal? May I hazard a guess that perhaps it is associated with the fact that oxygen is a free-radical acceptor and that in coals there are things rather like free radicals. It is possible that the suppression of the swelling properties of coals by oxidation is due to interaction of this kind between the coal and the oxygen. If this is so, one can consider other materials that behave in a similar way. It is known that many other additives, e.g. sulphur, nitric oxide, boric acid, etc., reduce coking. Reduction by solids can be achieved in a different way from that with oxygen. In the latter case it is necessary to heat the coal with oxygen before it is put into a mix for briquetting. Perhaps one of these other materials could be added to a mix including pitch etc., and carbonized together, without agglomeration occurring. Such a technique would seem to be preferable because it would avoid the oxidation heating cycle. I agree, of course, that one would not add sulphur, but I think one might be able to choose a more appropriate additive—probably inorganic—which does not cause a nuisance such as atmospheric pollution, high ash content or deposit formation.

In Fig. 5 Dr. Jenkins drew attention to the relation between the amount of oxygen used and the surface area of the coal. One would think that such a relation, over the small particle size range which appears to have been used, would be fortuitous. Perhaps Dr. Jenkins would explain how he measured the surface area with sufficient accuracy to justify the drawing of the curve.

AUTHOR:

On the first point by Mr. Bond, that of the fundamental mechanism; as I have explained, I am not at all familiar with the vast amount of work on this subject, nor am I familiar with the details of work which has been done at this establishment. My problem was the transmission of the process from the laboratory to the pilot plant stage. Mr. Bond points out that from the theory he has tentatively proposed for the fundamental mechanism it can be deduced that other substances can be used. This is quite true. One can prevent distortion and clustering of these briquettes by the addition of many chemicals. This might at first sight appear to be far cheaper than the oxidation process, but, of course, there is rather a rigid specification on the chemical which you can add. If it is an inorganic substance which is not volatile at carbonizing temperatures, then, for every 1% you add, the ash content of your carbonized briquette goes up by about $1\frac{1}{2}\%$ to 2%. It must be noncorrosive with regard to the materials of construction used in conventional carbonizing equipment. It must also be very cheap. There is work going on at CRE on the addition of such chemicals, and it is quite true that it will probably prove a serious rival to the oxidation process.

On the subject of rate of oxidation versus particle size, shown in Fig. 5, I would agree with Mr.

Bond that with only three points over a short range the drawing of a straight line is optimistic. For this reason I have shown it as a broken line. As regards the surface area determinations, perhaps the method could be explained by Mr. E. H. Williams of CRE who did the actual measurements.

MR. E. H. WILLIAMS (*National Coal Board, Stoke Orchard*):

Before presenting my prepared contribution, I would like to comment on Mr. Bond's remarks on Fig. 5 of Dr. Jenkins' paper. This graph indicates a relationship between the amount of oxygen consumed by Betteshanger coal at a given temperature, and the surface area of the coal used. His criticisms of this graph are justified, but it must be pointed out that the figure is for illustrative purposes, and that much more evidence exists which supports the concept that the behaviour of Betteshanger coal during oxidation in the temperature range 200°C to 400°C is greatly influenced by the surface area of the coal.

The choice of coal grinds used in the pilot-plant tests was limited by briquetting requirements, and the surface area was only varied from 300 sq. ft./lb. to 600 sq. ft./lb. These areas were calculated from sieve and subsieve analyses of the coal powder and in certain circumstances, were checked by practical measurements of the surface area, using an air permeability method; good agreement between the two methods was obtained.

The results indicated that surface area and temperature were the two chief variables affecting oxygen consumption and heat release. This work has been followed up by a series of small-scale tests (which are referred to later), using a batch fluidized reactor. These tests are still in progress, but results so far indicate a probable linear relationship between surface area and oxygen consumption over a four or five-fold range of surface area (approximately 400 sq. ft./lb. to 2000 sq. ft./lb.).

It is interesting to note that such phenomena as:

(a) the reappearance of caking properties in crushed oxidized coal,
(b) the effect of grinding on the infra-red spectrum of oxidized coal,

can be readily explained if it is assumed that the oxidation of Betteshanger coal is confined to the outer surface.

With regard to my prepared discussion contribution, Monsieur Boyer and Dr. Jenkins have disclosed interesting information on the controlled oxidation of coal at moderate temperatures. However, the papers appear to be contradictory in several respects, particularly on the question of the influence of contact time on the oxidation of coal. The apparent discrepancies are probably due to the fact that the French workers used a low-rank, high-volatile coking coal (approx. 35% V.M. d.a.f. basis) while at the Coal Research Establishment we have been using high rank coals (approx. 17% V.M. d.a.f. basis). It has become evident during our work that there are several important differences between the behaviour of high rank and low rank coals. Thus, as Monsieur Boyer showed in his Fig. 1, the oxygen consumption of a low-rank coal is proportional to the time of oxidation over a period of one to two hours in the temperature range 200°C to 240°C, whereas for Betteshanger coal of medium size grading (20% less than 76μ and 100% less than 300μ) the pilot oxidation plant results indicate that the oxidation of Betteshanger coal was not sensitive to time variations for contact times of ten to forty minutes and temperatures of 200°C to 400°C. The specific surface of the coal was, however, a very important factor in determining the extent of oxidation.

Again, the heat evolved per unit weight of oxygen consumed appears to be much less for a low-rank coal, and there are also differences in the distribution of the products of oxidation—a greater proportion of water being formed in the case of low-rank coals.

These apparent differences in oxidation behaviour could have an important bearing on the engineering and economic aspects of coal oxidation, and it was decided to compare the oxidation of two coals of different rank under comparable conditions. A low-rank coking coal (code number 702, 37% volatile matter) and the Betteshanger coal used on the pilot oxidation plant (code number 203/4, 17% volatile matter) were tested batch-wise in a small fluidized reactor. Various grinds of coal were used, and the test temperature was 300°C. The results of the tests showed clearly that for the low rank coal, the rate of oxygen consumption was independent of particle size, and for particles of less than 500μ contact times of up to 40 minutes and a rate of oxygen supply of 1 g/kg min are necessary. The behaviour of the Betteshanger semianthracite coal provided a marked contrast, for in this case, it was confirmed that the rate of oxygen consumption decreased rapidly after periods varying from ten to twenty minutes, depending on the external surface area of the coal used. It is, therefore, possible to saturate the surface of the Betteshanger coal with oxygen. It may also be possible to do this with a low-rank coal, but it would require an oxygen consumption at least three times that of Betteshanger coal to do so.

It therefore appears that the nature of the coal substance exerts an important influence on the kinetics of coal oxidation. Whether the differences are a matter of degree or are due to different reaction mechanisms has not been established, but in any event they will have to be considered when an oxidation process is designed.

Monsieur A. F. Boyer (*Centre d'Etudes et Recherches des Charbonnages de France, Verneuil*):

There is one remark I would like to make. This concerns the influence of the residence time and the differences between Dr. Jenkins's results and my own. I think it is a question of the coal, but chiefly also of the temperature range, since he worked at lower temperatures than we do.

With regard to Mr. Bond's suggestion of reaction of oxygen with free radicals in coal, I do not think that it is a question of free radicals.

The reaction of low-temperature cokes and chars with oxygen has been studied by electron paramagnetic resonance; it has been found that at room temperature the reaction is reversible. This is not the same as for the fixation of oxygen on coal or char.

INVESTIGATIONS INTO THE CARBONIZATION OF BRIQUETTES IN GERMANY

By Wilhelm Reerink

Steinkohlenbergbauverein, Essen, Germany

Summary—Since we are still using a technique for the briquetting of bituminous coals which has remained substantially unchanged for fifty years, it was considered necessary for the Western German Coal Industry to establish an experimental station, with presses of varying capacities and producing briquettes of varying shapes, so that detailed studies of the processes involved in briquetting bituminous coals with binders could be made and the technical methods used developed. It is intended to study the carbonization of briquettes, in connection with these briquetting studies, in various types of oven.

A special pitch developed in the Ruhr for use in briquetting is the so-called TPS (Teerpechschmelze). This binder is also said to be suitable for briquetting ores and coal-ore mixtures. Reference should be made in this connection to the process for the briquetting of oil-containing concentrates from the Convertol process; this new briquetting process has been developed by the Gesellschaft für Kohlentechnik.

The trials carried out before and during the last war, by Hock and Didier Works—in the manufacture of shaped coke from weakly-caking or noncaking coals are briefly summarized; the results of further work along the same lines are also described. Particular consideration is given to tests in the preparation of foundry coke, which gives increased efficiency in Cupola furnaces with a simultaneous economy in fuel. Carbonization of briquettes on travelling grates is also touched upon.

Finally, the experience gained in Western Germany in the preparation of coal-ore briquettes is discussed. The starting point was the New Jersey zinc process, which has been found to be suitable for other ores, after appropriate modifications.

The fact that the raw materials basis of the mining industry in Western Germany is entirely different from that of Great Britain explains why the problem of manufacturing formed coke or briquette coke is only of interest in Western Germany in special cases; moreover, this type of production is not likely to play an important part in addition to normal carbonization, as will be the case in Great Britain.

Résumé—Les procédés employés jusqu' ici pour l'agglomération de la houille sont restés dans une large mesure les mêmes pendant les derniers 50 ans. Le Steinkohlenbergbauverein a jugé nécessaire, en conséquent, d'ériger une installation expérimentale avec des presses à rendements différents, produisants des agglomérés en différents formes, dans le but de faire des études très approfondies du procédé d'agglomération de houille avec des liants et pour pouvoir développer la technique de traitement. On envisage, par la suite, à examiner aussi la cokéfaction des agglomérés dans de différents systèmes de fours.

Un brai spécial pour l'agglomération, appelé " Teerpechschmelze " a été développé dans la Ruhr. On croit que ce liant convienne pour l'agglomération des minerais et des mélanges de houille avec du minerai. On mentionne à ce propos le procédé développé par la Gesellschaft für Kohlentechnik pour agglomérer le concentré huileux provenant du procédé Convertol.

On traite brièvement les essais de Hock et des Didier-Werke (faits pendant la dernière guerre mondiale), pour fabriquer du coke moulé en houilles à pouvoir agglutinant faible ou nul, et on décrit les résultats de quelques travaux supplémentaires à ce sujet. Des essais à fabriquer de coke moulé de fonderie, donnant une augmentation de capacité et en même temps une économie en combustible, méritent une attention spéciale. On traite également un autre sujet, c'est la cokéfaction d'agglomérés sur grille mobile.

Finalement on traite des expériences gagnées en Allemagne Occidentale dans la fabrication d'agglomérés d'une mélange de houille avec du minerai. On a pris comme point de départ le procédé à zinc de la New Jersey Cy. Ce procédé, modifié d'une manière appropriée, convient aussi à d'autres minerais.

Comme les matières premières de l'industrie charbonnière de l'Allemagne Occidentale diffèrent essentiellement de celles de la Grande Bretagne, le problème de la fabrication de coke moulé, ou d'agglomérés carbonisés n'interesse pas l'Allemagne Occidentale que dans des cas particuliers, pendant qu'en Angleterre on doit s'occuper de ce problème assez minutieusement, a côté de la coké-faction normale.

Zusammenfassung—Da man bei der Steinkohlenbrikettierung heute noch eine Verfahrenstechnik anwendet, die im wesentlichen seit 50 Jahren unverändert ist, hat man es im westdeutschen Stein-kohlenbergbau für notwendig gehalten, eine Veruchsanlage mit Pressen verschiedener Leistung und Brikettform zu errichten, um den Brikettierungsvorgang von Steinkohlen mit Bindemitteln sehr eingehend studieren und due Verfahrenstecknik weiterentwickeln zu können. Es ist beabsichtigt, im Anschluss hieran auch die Verkokung der Briketts in verschiedenen Ofensystemen zu untersuchen.

Ein im Ruhrgebiet entwickeltes Spezialpech für die Brikettierung ist die sogenannte " Teerpech-schmelze ". Dieses Bindemittel soll sich auch für die Brikettierung von Erzen und von Kohle-Erz-Gemischen eignen. Erwähnt wird in diesem Zusammenhang auch das von der Gesellschaft für Kohlentechnik entwickelte Verfahren zur Brikettierung von ölhaltigen Konzentraten aus dem Convertolverfahren.

Die vor und während des letzten Krieges von Hock und den Didier-Werken durchgefuhrten Versuche zur Herstellung von Formkoks aus schwach- oder nichtbackenden Kohlen werden kurz behandelt und die Ergebnisse weiterer, in ähnlicher Richtung liegender Arbeiten werden beschrieben. Besondere Beachtung verdienen die Versuche zur Herstellung von Giesserei-Formkoks, der im Kupolofen Leistungsteigerung bei gleichzeitiger Brennstoffeinsparung erzielt. Auch die Verkokung von Briketts auf dem Wanderrost wird behandelt.

Schliesslich wird auf die Erfahrung eingegangen, die man in Westdeutschland mit der Herstellung von Kohle-Erz-Briketts gewonnen hat. Hierbei ging man von dem New-Jersey-Zinkverfahren aus, das sich in entsprechender Abwandlung auch fur andere Erze eignet.

Die völlig anders geartete rohstoffliche Grundlage des Kohlenbergbaus in Westdeutschland im Vergleich zu der in Grossbritannien führt dazu, dass das Problem der Herstellung von Formkoks oder Brikettkoks in Westdeutschland nur in Sonderfällen Interesse findet, nicht aber berufen ist, wie in England neben der Normalverkokung eine grössere Rolle zu spielen.

ALTHOUGH the thermal treatment of briquettes made from brown coal, bituminous coal or from mixtures of bituminous coal with ore—by means of low-temperature carbonization or coking—has been practised in Germany over a long period, the application of the processes employed has not hitherto been on a very large scale in Western Germany. It is clear that the reason for this is that the proportion of coking coal in the total production from German mines is considerably greater than that in other countries. In consequence of this there is no need for the Western German coal-mining districts to concern themselves with the manufacture of coke from high-volatile, weakly caking or noncaking coals to any particular extent. Thus, when German engineers began to study the manufacture of " shaped coke " by carbonizing briquettes, some twenty years ago, this was principally on behalf of the Central German brown-coal and Upper Silesian bituminous-coal mining industries. Even earlier than this, studies had been made in Germany of another process, which involved briquetting certain ores together with coal and carbonizing the briquettes so obtained; the intention was to achieve simultaneously a means of making fine-grained ores adhere together in lumps and ensuring an intimate mixing of the ore to be reduced with the reducing medium. In the meantime, investigations have been made in various places as to how briquetting can be improved and, in individual cases, large scale development work on the carbonization of briquettes made of low-volatile coal has been carried out.

In my paper I should like to give a brief survey of the experience which we have gained in this field, but without referring to the low-temperature or medium-temperature carbonization of brown-coal briquettes, since this aspect has been adequately treated in the literature, and, in addition, the subject would not be of interest in this conference, which is particularly concerned with bituminous coals. In the first place

I should like to deal with a number of questions concerning briquetting; following upon this, I shall write of the experience we have gained in carbonizing briquettes made from noncaking coals, and I shall finally deal with carbonization tests on briquettes manufactured from a mixture of coal and ore.

1. *Problems of Briquetting Technique*

In several studies of the carbonization of briquettes made from bituminous coal or of mixtures of bituminous coal with ores, it has repeatedly been observed that various factors govern the quality of the carbonized briquettes; in addition to the carbonization conditions, the briquetting technique used and the binder employed, as well as the physical characteristics of the material briquetted, are of decisive importance.

When employing normal bituminous-coal-tar pitch—softening point 65°C to 75°C—which is normally used by us as a binder in briquetting bituminous coal, the height of the carbonization residue in the crucible is, according to our findings, a rather reliable index of the behaviour of the binder during carbonization of the briquettes. The greater the residue from the binder after carbonization, the higher will be the strength of the carbonized briquettes; nevertheless, for good briquettes, a large quantity of carbonization residue must not be combined with an excessively high softening point of the binder. It is well known that difficulties occur, during normal briquetting of bituminous coal, if the softening point of the pitch is higher than 75°C. However, in order to be able to make full use of the advantage of a high carbonization residue in the case of raw materials which are particularly difficult to make into briquettes, we have tried the effect of adding various mixtures of tar oils and hard pitch to the briquetting mixture, the hard pitch—with a softening point up to more than 100°C—being added in a ground state to the coal to be briquetted. The mixture of coal and hard pitch is then mixed with a similar quantity of a suitable oil, in which the hard pitch is soluble. Following this, the mixture is heated and briquetted in the usual manner. In special cases it is even possible to dispense with the heating, so that briquetting can be carried out at the normal temperature. In addition, we have found that when petroleum-refinery residues are used, the suitability of the binder for the briquette carbonization process can still be assessed from the height of the carbonization residue. Again, in certain cases where refinery wastes are employed, it will be more advisable to employ a product which has a high softening point and can be added in a ground state; the briquetting operation is then carried out after the addition of the oils.

This addition of oils to binding media of high softening point, to which I have just referred, can of course also take place during the preparation of the coal. It has thus been found advantageous, in individual cases, to de-ash and de-water coal slurries by the Convertol process, by phase reversal; following this, the oil-containing concentrate is briquetted, after the addition of ground hard pitch, either with or without the admixture of fine ores or small coal. In this way it is possible to ensure that the oil, in the first place, becomes effective during the preparation of the slurry and is also active during the briquetting operation. We could conceive that, provided certain prerequisite conditions were assured, this procedure might even eliminate the thermal drying of the concentrate.

The Pluto Chemical Works of the Rheinelbe Bergbau-AG in Gelsenkirchen have been occupied, in the last few years, in developing a special pitch—derived from bituminous coal tar—for use in briquetting. This special pitch, a patented brand, is called in German " Teerpechschmelze " or, in abbreviated form, TPS. TPS is a mixture of normal pitch and tar oils, with the addition of a certain amount of crystallized aromatic compounds. One of the principal advantages of using this material is said to lie in the fact that it eliminates the need for drying the material to be briquetted. At the same time, when this TPS is used the quantity of binder required is claimed to be from 25% to 35% less than usual, so that the fact that the price of TPS is higher than ordinary pitch would be more than compensated by this saving. This product is used at present in the Ruhr in a plant which manufactures " ovoid " briquettes from bituminous coal. In this installation, the TPS is injected—in a fluid state and at a temperature of 145°C to 150°C—into the coal to be briquetted. It is said that good results have been obtained for several months by the addition of not more than 5·3% to 5·4% of TPS, whereas 7·2% to 7·5% were required when using normal pitch as the binding medium. In tests with the low-shaft furnace TPS has also been used on a large scale as a binder for briquetting a mixture of fine ores, coal and limestone. The moisture content of the material to be briquetted in this instance was approximately 8%. It was found that 5·5% of TPS was sufficient to allow of the production of briquettes which were capable of being directly smelted in the low-shaft furnace without previous thermal treatment. It should be emphasized that, in this case, it is necessary that the briquettes be particularly strong, since they must be able to go through the low-shaft furnace without being crushed; at the same time they must possess a high reactivity. As far as I know it has not been possible up to now to achieve this with other binders.

Furthermore, semicommercial-scale tests have shown that TPS is suitable for briquetting quite a number of very different fine-grained ores without previous drying. This method seems to be less expensive than sintering the ores. It can be expected, therefore, that TPS will, in the future, play a certain part in the production of shaped coke or ore briquettes, and this is the reason why I thought it worth while to draw attention to these findings of the Pluto Chemical Works.

In the studies which we have carried out in recent years on behalf of the Association for Coal Technology (Gesellschaft für Kohlentechnik) and of the Steinkohlenbergbauverein, we have repeatedly observed that the process of briquetting itself remains, to a very large extent, unexplored. Since it is, unfortunately, impossible to reproduce the briquetting process on a small scale while still maintaining all the conditions of large-scale operation—so as to be able to draw experimentally established conclusions as to methods of improving briquetting—we decided to set up a large experimental installation for the briquetting of bituminous coal. This plant, a layout diagram of which is given in Fig. 1, is being erected at the present time at an idle colliery in the Essen district. This installation will be equipped with the most modern machines, including several types of press, devices for crushing, screening, preparing, and drying the coal to be briquetted, as well as several bunkers with feeding devices and some mixers. Thus we shall be able to manufacture, under commercial conditions, 5 tons to 15 tons of briquettes per hour, the weight of the individual briquettes being 20, 50, or 1000 grams. The experimental plant will be completed at the end of this year; its principal task will be to provide a basis for improvements in the methods of briquetting bituminous coal. Since we are already manufacturing more than 7,000,000 tons of briquettes in Western Germany, using dry steam coals —the briquettes being used for domestic heating—the demand for briquetting pitch has increased so considerably that we shall not have sufficient quantities of tar pitch

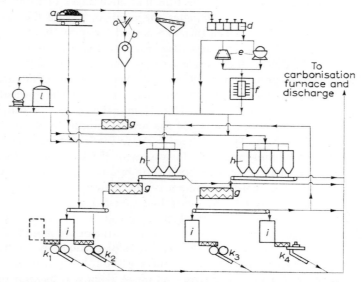

FIG. 1—Experimental plant for trials of briquetting and briquette carbonization

a. Test coal	h. Storage and Proportioner
b. Crushing	i. Pug-mill
c. Screening plant	K1. 20 g press (5t/hr)
d. Flotation	K2. 50 g press (5t/hr)
e. Dewatering	K3. 20 g press (15t/hr)
f. Drier	K4. 1 kg press (7t/hr)
g. Mixer	L. Heating vessel for liquid binder.

for other purposes, unless we can succeed in reducing the consumption of binder in briquetting. We hope, that other problems too, in connection with the carbonization of briquettes, can be studied by means of this experimental plant.

2. *Carbonization of Briquettes Made from Noncaking Coal*

More than twenty years ago, detailed studies had been made in Germany on the manufacture of formed coke prepared by carbonizing briquettes, and these trials were, primarily, carried out in the interests of the Central German brown-coal industry and the Upper Silesian bituminous-coal industry. I must particularly refer in this connection to the work carried out by H. Hock of Clausthal and K. Baum of the Didier-Werke A.G., who showed in large-scale tests that, by using the so-called two-stage process, it is possible to produce high-grade coke from noncaking coal. Their proposals envisaged the treatment of the high-volatile, noncaking, brown or bituminous coals in the following way: the coals are first carbonized—at low or medium temperatures—and the resulting coke (ground to suitable size) briquetted

F<small>IG</small>. 2.

F<small>IG</small>. 3.

with 8% to 12% of caking bituminous coal, tar pitch being added as a binder; these briquettes are then hardened in a second thermal treatment. In actual fact, therefore, what we have here is not a two-stage process but a three-stage process with two separate thermal treatments. I think I may take it that the results of these studies are known, since several publications on the subject have been made.[1] During the last war large-scale tests were planned in order to prove the suitability of this coke for metallurgical use, but they were not carried out. By contrast, good results were obtained at that time from tests of the fitness of this shaped coke for use in cupola furnaces. The utility of this process will be greatest where strongly caking bituminous coals are rare—and are therefore expensive—and where large quantities of cheap, high-volatile, weakly caking or noncaking bituminous coal or brown coal are available. In addition to this, interest in the process will increase considerably as soon as it is possible to reduce the costs, by developing modern methods of degasifying the raw coal and of hardening the briquettes. Various possibilities of achieving this end are already in existence. For the first degasification stage, the most promising processes are, in my opinion, the fluidized carbonization process of the Pittsburgh Consolidation Coal Company and the Lurgi-Ruhrgas process (LR-process). In addition to indirectly-heated vertical-chamber or inclined-chamber ovens, it is possible to use furnaces which are directly heated, such as the cross-flow oven of the Dr. C. Otto Company.

Since we in Western Germany produce only a very small proportion of high-volatile, weakly caking coals, these developments in processing techniques are (as I have already pointed out) only of marginal interest. Nevertheless, we shall have the opportunity to erect—in association with the experimental plant for briquetting described above—several degasification furnaces, so as to be able to carry out trials of this kind on a fairly large scale.

a) *Production of formed foundry coke.* Starting from the experience gained with coal ceramic material, W. Schreiber of the Hannover-Hannibal A.G. Steinkohlenbergwerk has carried out large-scale trials in the manufacture of briquettes of various sizes using a normal coke breeze with the addition of a few per cent of bituminous coal and 7% to 8% of a mixture of tar and pitch; these briquettes, when subsequently hardened in the tunnel furnaces, in the vertical-chamber oven, or in the cross-flow oven of Dr. C. Otto, give a very firm coke. (Figs. 2 and 3.)

When these medium or large-size shaped cokes—with standard weights of 400 g 1 kg or 3 kg—were tried out in the cupola furnace, a reduction of the quantity of coke per charge of up to 30% and more was achieved with a simultaneous increase of 35% and more in the smelting efficiency of the furnace. This shaped coke was used in cupola furnaces of very different sizes, and also in hot-blast furnaces, marked advantages being obtained in all cases. This formed foundry coke is characterized by a particularly low degree of combustibility, so that it does not react with the hot carbon dioxide already in the shaft; it only burns and develops its full smelting heat in the area around the blast jets. Accordingly, the CO content of the waste gases was generally less than 5% and the temperature at the top of the furnace was not so high. The low combustibility is governed by the small pore space and by other structural properties, which give rise to a low and smooth surface area in relation to the volume.

It is intended to continue these large-scale tests in order to obtain experience in the manufacture and use of special formed coke of this kind.

b) *Carbonization of anthracite briquettes.* The collaboration in planning and building a large-scale experimental installation for the carbonization of anthracite briquettes carried out (inside Germany) by German companies, at the instigation of the K. Baum Company, resulted in very valuable experience on the possibilities of combining the Convertol process for the preparation of fine-grained coal with subsequent briquetting and briquette carbonization. The task was particularly difficult, since the coal to be treated possessed several properties which were completely unfamiliar to us. In addition to this, we had to use a particular grade of asphalt as a binder and this asphalt behaved in a completely different fashion from the tar pitches. Finally, the trial operations also gave valuable information about the most suitable dimensions of the vertical-chamber oven in relation to the size of briquette. After overcoming numerous difficulties we succeeded in producing in the experimental plant up to 40 tons daily of briquette coke with an ash content of from 8% to 10%; the quality of this coke appears to be capable of improvement by means of further trial work, so that it can now be successfully used in foundry blast furnaces.

At the present moment German firms are—with our collaboration—engaged elsewhere outside Germany, in erecting a large experimental plant for the preparation of a heavily interstratified, noncaking coal, which is, however, of very high volatile content. The preparation is followed by subsequent low-temperature carbonization, followed in turn by briquetting of the low-temperature coke and carbonization of the briquettes. In this plant we shall be able to apply all the experience gained hitherto to the fullest possible extent.

c) *Carbonization of bituminous coal briquettes **on a travelling grate.*** It is well known that rather early large-scale attempts have been made in the USA and in Canada to carbonize coal and briquettes on a travelling grate. In Canada, Mr. Andersen,[2] of the Shawinigan Chemicals Limited, successfully used a travelling grate for the manufacture of carbide coke from bituminous coal; in the USA, the New Jersey Zinc Company employed an under-feed stoker for the carbonization of zinc ore/coal briquettes.[3] According to information received from Kurt Baum, 8 grate-carbonization plants of the Shawinigan type, each with a throughput of 75 tons of coal per day, are running in Canada, whereas in South Africa a larger plant with a throughput of 120 tons per day for the manufacture of carbide coke has been in continuous operation for a couple of years. As for the New Jersey Zinc Company process, 6 plants are in operation in the United States and Europe. At the recommendation of Baum, the Steinmuller Company, using a Shawinigan licence and deriving profit from additional experience gathered by the K. Baum Company, has set up a small grate-carbonization plant at one of our experimental installations; this is intended, in the first instance, for carbonization tests with various coals.

On this grate we carried out a number of tests with bituminous coal briquettes. It is said that this process modifies the fixed carbon content as little as possible and makes briquettes which are capable of withstanding storage and transport. The grate-carbonizing plant (Fig. 4) works in the following manner:

An air-cooled grate which is sealed—along its long side against a water-cooled wall—moves in a furnace of refractory material. Suitable devices permit of adjusting the speed of movement of the grate and the height of the coal on the grate. The speed of the grate can be varied from 44 mm/min to 340 mm/min ($1\frac{3}{4}$ in./min to $13\frac{1}{2}$ in./min). The adjustability for height provides for a thickness of coal of from 0 to 220 mm (0 to $8\frac{1}{2}$ in.); the effective heating area is 4·45 sq. m (48 sq. ft.). Air can be blown, in controlled quantities, through the grate from a series of air chambers. The gases leave the furnace via a flue above the coal inlet; the coke is discharged at

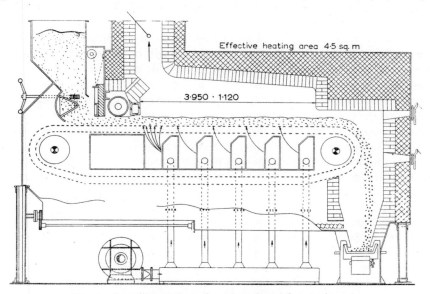

Effective heating area 4·5 sq. m

3·950 · 1·120

FIG. 4—Travelling-grate carbonizing plant (after Andersen).

the end of the grate on to a water-cooled shaker trough, which guides the carbonized material through a water spray into the intermediate bunker and to the loading point. Underneath the grate a discharge device is provided to remove from the furnace any material which may fall through the bars. In future, however, this discharging device will no longer be necessary, because the gaps between the grate bars are so small that, even during tests with noncaking small coal, no material fell through the grate.

Before beginning a test, the furnace is brought to the desired carbonization temperature by burning fuel on the grate. When the various temperature indicators located in the furnace show that the arch has reached the proper temperature, the material to be carbonized is fed on to the grate.

This process has been called " autogenous carbonization " by Kurt Baum.[4] In contrast to other carbonization processes it works without a supply of additional heat, the temperature and the heat required for the degasification of the coal being produced by partial combustion—or rather gasification—of the volatile matter which is released during the thermal decomposition. Thus, only two products are obtained from autogenous carbonization, namely:

(1) the hot degasified residue,

(2) the volatile matter, transformed by partial combustion with air.

Provided that the hot combustion gases can be directly utilized, the only " losses " are, therefore, the sensible heat of the coke, the latent heat in the vaporized surface water and in the water formed by the reactions in the furnace, and losses due to radiation and conduction. With good waste-heat recovery, the thermal efficiency is equal to that of the most modern types of coke oven.

When coal with more than 20% volatile matter is carbonized, its partial combustion will result in the production of a poor quality gas of 750 kcal/m³ to 800 kcal/m³ (78 B.t.u./cu. ft. to 84 B.t.u./cu. ft.).

The volatile matter content of briquettes made of subbituminous or semibituminous coal is less than 20%; nevertheless there will be suffcient heat available for carbonizing briquettes with as little as 10% of volatile matter, if use is also made of the sensible heat contained in the gas. This was ascertained by tests upon subbituminous and semibituminous coal (10% to 12% and 12% to 19% volatile matter, according to the German classification) and on briquettes of both types of coal.

The advantages of travelling-grate carbonization are as follows: very low capital costs, high throughput and very high speed of carbonization. In addition, labour costs, consumption of materials and maintenance costs are low; on the other hand, its value is diminished by the fact that no byproducts are obtained apart from the poor gas.

3. *Preparation and Carbonization of Coal-Ore Briquettes*

More than twenty years ago I had the opportunity to collaborate in the introduction of the New Jersey Zinc Company's process in a German zinc smelting works and this gave me a chance to collect much interesting knowledge. In the New Jersey process—a flowsheet of which is reproduced in Fig. 5—the zinc ore is thoroughly mixed with 40% to 50% of a strongly caking coal and briquetted, sulphite liquor being used as a binder.

These coal-ore briquettes are carbonized at some 800°C in a cross-flow oven, a very high rate of heating being applied; the carbonized briquettes are then immediately heated to 1250°C in a vertical-chamber oven lined with carborundum bricks, so that the zinc ore is reduced and the metallic zinc sublimated. The carbonized briquettes made from the mixture of zinc ore and coal, must be strong enough to " stand the journey " through the vertical-chamber oven, during the zinc-removal process. The briquette residues which contain no zinc must still have a certain measure of strength when they are discharged from the zinc-removal furnace. In the large-scale tests carried out in the German zinc-smelting industry before the introduction of this process, it became clear that the best values were obtained with the American ore and American coal, and that with one American and one German component, results which were still staisfactory could be obtained. However, at first, even after extensive tests, no success was obtained using German ore and German coal. It was later discovered that even the best German coal was far poorer in caking power than the corresponding American coal. At the same time, the German zinc ore was a sintered product, with a much more porous surface and much lower strength than the sandy, unsintered, and nonporous American zinc ore. Good results with both components

—coal as well as zinc ore—of German origin were only obtained after the caking-bitumen content of the mixture had been artificially increased by adding a few per cent of hard pitch. This showed very clearly that both the binder—in this case the caking bitumen—and the physical properties of the material to be briquetted—in this case the zinc ore—may exert a great influence during the carbonization of briquettes.

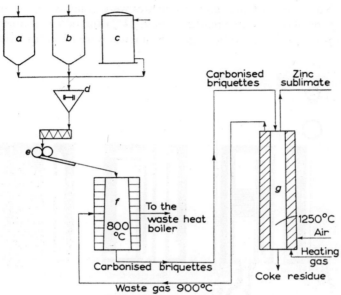

FIG. 5—New Jersey Zinc-recovery process

a. Zinc ore
b. Coal
c. Sulphate waste solution
d. Pug-mill
e. Briquetting press
f. Carbonization furnace
g. Zinc removal furnace.

TABLE 1

Screen Analysis of Five Different Fine Ores

Ore No.	1	2	3	4	5
Size mm	%	%	%	%	%
+ 3	0·1	1·4	6·1	6·1	—
3 — 1	10·6	11·2	20·0	21·7	—
1 — 0·5	20·6	17·9	18·3	15·6	—
0·5 — 0·2	28·4	20·4	33·6	29·1	3·2
0·2 — 0·1	18·5	13·0	20·3	25·5	35·5
0·1 — 0·075	7·6	10·4 ⎱	1·7	2·0	12·9
— 0·075	14·2	25·7 ⎰			48·4

We recalled these trials when we were faced with the task of making—from a fine-grained ore—briquettes containing not more than 10% to 12% of coal, for subsequent carbonization at 600°C to 700°C, ordinary pitch being used as a binder.

D

The fine ores used in the individual briquetting tests were, as Table 1 shows, of very different size distribution.

The coal used for the purpose of briquetting was added as dust, either coking-coal dust with 24% volatile matter or low-volatile coal with 16% volatile matter, depending on the properties of the ore to be briquetted.

From ore No. 3, for instance, good briquettes were obtained by the admixture of 10% of coking coal dust, (volatile matter content 24%) and of 6% of normal tar pitch. After low-temperature carbonization, these briquettes were found to have the desired

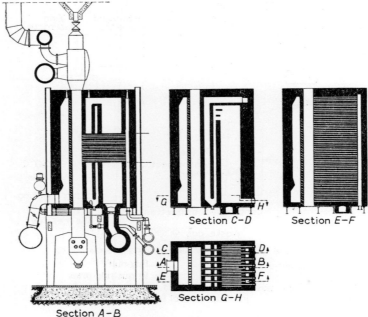

FIG. 6—Cross-flow Shaft Furnace of Dr. C. Otto Co.

ratio of ore to carbon and to be of satisfactory strength. By contrast, when briquetting ore No. 4 (whose particle size distribution was about the same as that of ore No. 3) with addition of the same coal and pitch, and maintaining the same mixing ratio, it was found that the green briquettes came up to expectations—but after carbonization under the same conditions they would cluster. What now was the reason for this different behaviour of the briquettes during carbonization? Microscopic examination revealed that the particles of ore No. 3 were too weak to stand up to the pressure exerted upon them by the briquetting press, whereas ore No. 4 was not crushed in the press. In consequence, a larger quantity of binder was needed to cover the larger total surface of ore created by crushing in the case of the weaker ore No. 3. This observation was confirmed by the fact that the briquettes of ore No. 4 could be carbonized without any difficulty or clustering, when they were made of a mixture in which the caking coal had been replaced by a coal containing not more than 16% volatile matter.

The briquetting of these mixtures caused no difficulties, so long as segregation was avoided, e.g. by eliminating any intermediate bunkering. The bulk weights of ore to coal dust were in the ratio 1660 to 700. Even the very fine ore No. 5, with 50% below 0·075 mm, was successfully briquetted with the addition of 5% to 6% of soft pitch and 14% of coking coal dust. Carbonization of these briquettes at a temperature of 600°C transformed them into a well-shaped material suitable for the smelter.

The first trials of low-temperature carbonization " on the ton scale " were carried out in a directly heated experimental furnace. The heating gases flowed around the briquettes, entering the carbonization chamber on all sides through orifices in the walls. The furnace was operated batchwise and usable low-temperature carbonized briquettes were obtained. The positive results of this carbonization trial led to the manufacture of more than 1,000 tons of coal-ore briquettes, which were subsequently carbonized in the cross-flow oven of the Dr. Otto Company (Fig. 6), to which I have referred earlier in this paper. The carbonization chamber in this furnace—which was 2 metres (6 ft. 6 in.) broad, 0·6 metres (2 ft.) deep and 6·5 metres (21 ft.) in effective height—was heated with generator gas. Finally, after a series of tests, up to 75% of the heating gases was led from above into the freshly-charged briquettes, so as to accelerate markedly the rate of heating up to 600°C. Carbonization was carried out at temperatures below 700°C.

This is, in brief, a survey of some of the investigations which have been carried out in Western Germany during the last years. We understand that the problems which the N.C.B. is facing in the field of briquette carbonization are much more urgent and important, and I shall be very glad indeed, if you can find some useful suggestions in my report on our modest tests and efforts.

REFERENCES

1. REED F. H., *U.S. Bur. Mines, Inf. Circ.* 7462 (June 1948).
   THAU A., *Coke & Gas* **10**, 397–402 (Nov. 1948).
2. ANDERSEN A. H., *Trans. Canad. Inst. Min. Met.* 139–151 (1944). U.S. Patent 2,380,930 (5 October 1942).
3. U.S. Patent 2,536,365 (2 January 1951)
4. BAUM K., World Power Conf., Sectional Conf., Rio de Janiero (1954).
   Brennst.-Warmekr. No. 7, 244–249 (1954).

DISCUSSION

MR. J. C. A. KAYE (*National Coal Board, Stoke Orchard*):

In his discussion of the problems of briquetting technique, Dr. Reerink has stated that the height of the carbonization residue in the crucible is a very reliable index of the behaviour of the binder during carbonization of the briquettes. I am not quite sure whether Dr. Reerink is referring to the weight of residue or the volume of the residue.

Then, Dr. Reerink has described at some length the use of what we call a cut-back pitch. I was particularly interested to note that in certain cases the hard pitch could be added to coal which had been previously treated with the oils, i.e. the cutting back of the pitch operation could be attained *in situ*. Would Dr. Reerink express any preference as to when the pitch and oils should be added? I should have thought that it would have been preferable to mix the oils and pitch before adding them to the coal. This conclusion has been reached after a considerable number of experiments here at the Coal Research Establishment. We have been interested in using low-softening-point binders for several reasons. We have, however, preferred to use topped tar (softening point 40°C to 45°C (R & B)) as the binder. This is, in effect, the residue obtained from the distillation of a crude tar at a temperature of approximately 300°C. With the particular coals we have briquetted we find that the total binder consumption, using this topped tar, is lower than when we used a cut-back pitch, particularly if the oil used to cut back the pitch was added to the coal before the pitch.

Much has been written about the effect of moisture on the briquetting of coal with a binder. It was interesting to note that Dr. Reerink claims that with a cut-back pitch even wet raw materials can be briquetted without difficulty. I should like to ask Dr. Reerink what was the moisture content of the mixture briquetted and particularly what type of press was used.

In our research experience, pitch is a satisfactory binder for both wet and dry coals, provided that similar briquetting temperatures and pressures are used in each case. In practice, however, satisfactory briquettes are not obtained from wet coal mixtures unless additional pitch is added to improve the product. Has Dr. Reerink modified his technique in any way so as to overcome this difficulty of compressing an unsuitably plastic mixture without the use of additional pitch?

I should like to say here that on small scale experiments we have found that emulsified petroleum bitumen binders are particularly suitable for briquetting wet coal. We have achieved in batch experiments, with coal of up to 20% moisture, a reduction of approximately 40% in the amount of binder required compared with tests in which solid bitumen was used. Moreover, the briquetting stage with emulsified binders was carried out at atmospheric temperatures.

AUTHOR:

Mr. Kaye has asked three questions. The first referred to the statement in my paper that the height of the carbonization residue in the crucible is a reliable index of the behaviour of the binder during the carbonization of briquettes. To make the point clear, I should like to put it in this way: the coke yield of a tar pitch determined in the same way as the coke yield of a coking coal, in a platinum crucible, gives a very reliable indication of the behaviour and the value of a tar pitch to be used as binder.

As for the second question whether I would prefer to mix the oil and the tar pitch before adding them to the coal or to add the pitch to a coal previously treated with oil, I should like to state that according to our experience the consumption of binder is about the same in both cases. As a rule, technical conditions will make it imperative to add the pitch after the oil because in existing briquetting plants the pitch has to be ground before adding it to the coal. Now, if we mix pitch and oil this would lead to a reduction of the softening point of the pitch and would make grinding impossible. Thus, there is only the choice between rebuilding the whole plant so that pitch with a lower softening point can be used or, on the other hand, using ground hard pitch which means that pitch and oil have to be added separately. When briquetting coal which has been cleaned by the Convertol Process the oil has to be added during the preparation stage for separating the coal slurries from the dirt and it goes without saying that the pitch required for briquetting has to be added to the oily coal.

By the way, I wish to emphasize that the special pitch mentioned in my paper and called TPS is not the same as normal cut-back pitch. It is characterized by a certain content of aromatic compounds containing more than one ring and this composition is claimed to be the decisive factor for its good behaviour when used as a binder and for its excellent wetting properties.

This leads me to Mr. Kaye's last question concerning the moisture content of the briquetting mixture. As far as I know, successful tests have been made with coal of up to 8% moisture content briquetted in normal presses. At present, large-scale experiments are under way in Germany, using emulsions of tar pitch and water, which seem to be rather promising. We succeeded in producing strong briquettes by means of this type of binder. However, these investigations are still in the experimental stage and further research work is necessary before final conclusions are drawn.

DR.-ING. KURT BAUM (*Dr.-Ing. Kurt Baum & Co., Essen*):

I am a Consulting Engineer in the field of coal preparation, briquetting and carbonization, and the chemical conversion of coal. I have heard with great interest the excellent survey of results obtained in Germany with the carbonization of briquettes, as presented by Dr.-Ing. W. Reerink. For completeness' sake, I wanted to make a few remarks, since I have been working in this field—that is, on the manufacture of " shaped " coke—for about twenty years. As we have heard, the first step is to obtain a good briquette, i.e. a good raw briquette which meets the requirements of the normal physical standards. I have often heard the term a " carbonizable briquette ". This expression is rather confusing, since we expect the carbonizing process to lead to another conversion and upgrading of the product; this conversion would produce e.g. greater hardness or greater resistance to abrasion. The ingredients used for the briquetting, and their behaviour during coking, are most important; " carbonizability " is greatly affected by variations in coking temperature and heating rate. I will cite a few examples:

Here in England there is a special interest in so-called smokeless fuel; in this case, coal of low- to medium-volatile content or semi-coke fines form the raw material, which is briquetted with pitch and/or coking coal. However, some volatile matter has to be left after carbonization, so as to allow of easy ignition. Consequently, we do not need the high temperatures used in ordinary coking.

Another application is that of metallurgical coke. Blast-furnace operators are not enthusiastic about this " compressed coke ". As we have seen, a porosity of from some 30% to a maximum of 40% is the optimum value to be obtained after coking; such values give a coke of very low reactivity, of high density and correspondingly high bulk density. This coke is excellent for cupola smelting, but is less suitable for blast-furnace operations.

After long years of experimenting, however, we are now able to produce a " formed coke " with a porosity of up to 65%; this coke also has a high shatter index (94%) and a good abrasion index (90% or greater).

These are a few examples of the great variability of coking conditions. The variable factors are: temperature range and rate of heating for mixtures—which constitute, in themselves, yet another variable—while " cokeability " has to be related to all of these.

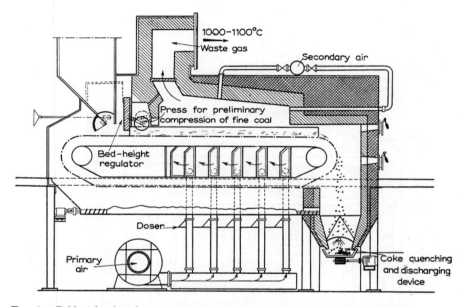

FIG. A—Grid carbonizer for autogenous carbonization of hard-coal, brown coal and lignite.

The cokeability (or carbonizability) is—in connection with our present subject, " shaped " coke— a matter which should be treated very differently from conventional coking, if it is ever to become an economical method. In my opinion, briquettes should be carbonized for 20 minutes to 100 minutes (the latter value being a maximum), according to their weight and size, i.e. from 10 to 1000 grams each. We must therefore think in terms of minutes, rather than hours. The short heating times can be obtained either by direct heat transfer from hot gases or preheated solids, or, in certain cases, by so-called " autogenous coking ".

This brings us back to the reaction with oxygen which we discussed this morning, but here more oxygen is introduced to cause partial combustion and, thus, bring about higher temperatures. The Shawinigan autogenous coking process has shown that, by the addition of a limited amount of air— in fact, about half the air required for combustion of the volatile matter given off during coking—we can easily achieve temperatures of 1200°C, and can carbonize coal or small briquettes (up to 20 grams) in some 20 minutes to 30 minutes; larger pieces require more time, up to 60 minutes, without burning fixed carbon. Not all raw briquettes, however, will stand up to the heating rate involved, which is at least 20°C per minute. A recent trial application of the same process has shown that there is a possibility at least, that this autogenous coking process will be applicable to medium-temperature carbonization.

Finally, I would like to demonstrate how the installation had to be modified. Fig. A shows a typical autogenous coker similar to the one shown in Fig. 4 of Dr. Reerink's paper. In this plant, air is admitted into various zones of the bed of coal during its travel through the coking chamber. The advantage of such a carbonizer is that it can be heated up in four hours; this is done by simply burning off the volatiles from the starting-up fuel. Once the brick-work has reached a temperature of 1000°C, carbonization may be started; it may be stopped at any time. The theoretical temperature produced by combustion of air containing 21 % of oxygen is approximately 1200°C, which is just right for high-temperature carbonization. The flue gas—with a fuel of 20 % volatile content (coal or briquettes) or higher—is of blast-furnace gas quality (750 kcal/m³ to 850 kcal/m³). If the coal is of lower volatile content, say 10 %, more complete combustion is necessary, until a point is reached where there is virtually no potential heat in the gas, and "near-reducing" conditions are attained.

In order to obtain lower reaction temperatures, it is necessary to supply the primary air with a higher content of N_2, i.e. the O_2 content is reduced from 21 % to 16 % to 17 %; as a result, the theoretical reaction temperature is reduced to somewhere between 800°C and 750°C.

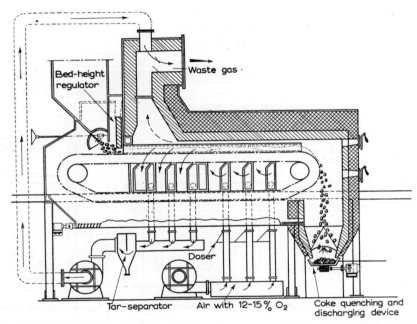

FIG. B—Grid carbonizing plant for the autogenous carbonization of hard-coal briquettes.

If domestic briquettes of the type mentioned this morning—with 14 % volatile content (including binder volatiles) of which 4 % to 5 % are to be left in the carbonized product (so that 10 % of volatile has to be removed)—the process can still be worked "autogenously". This means that it can take place without an external heat supply, since the hot reaction gases—at a temperature of about 700°C—can be recycled under heat-exchange condition, through the ingoing charge, and sensible heat is transferred to the raw ingoing briquettes. The required modifications are illustrated in Fig. B.

Figs. C and D show respectively, the raw and finished products obtained so far.

To sum up, I think that controlled partial combustion with oxygen at a temperature much higher than those discussed this morning will give a definite possibility of using a continuous "autogenous" process for the rapid conversion of coal into coke; this process may open up a new field of coking practice, which would soon compete with conventional indirectly-heated coke ovens, which have a normal heating rate of 1·5°C/min to 3°C/min.

MR. J. L. M. LAUNDER (*National Coal Board, Stoke Orchard*):

Dr. Reerink refers in his paper to the successful results he has obtained in briquetting difficult coals by using a mixture of tar oil and hard pitch as binder. I find this interesting because in some exploratory work carried out some years ago, a striking improvement was observed in the quality of

FIG. C—Ovoid briquettes—uncarbonized

FIG. D—Ovoid briquettes—carbonized

briquettes made from anthracite blends for subsequent carbonization, when a small quantity of an oil was incorporated in the normal briquetting mixture of coal and coal-tar pitch of softening point about 75°C.

Our tests were not exhaustive but they indicated that:

(1) the best results were obtained by first spraying the coal with the oil before blending with the pitch, and

(2) an increase in strength of the briquettes resulted when either a tar oil or a petroleum oil was used.

The improvement in the quality of the briquettes is illustrated in the following table:

	Test 1	Test 2	Test 3
Briquetting Mixture			
Pitch Content	7%	7%	7%
Oil Addition:			
(*a*) Tar oil	nil	8 pints/ton	nil
(*b*) Petroleum oil	nil	nil	8 pints/ton
Quality of Briquettes			
Abrasion Index*	73·6	85·6	84·0
Mean Breaking Load (lb.)	210	280	300

* Standard Abrasion Test as described in B.S. 1016—1942 except that the drum was rotated for 250 revolutions.

The briquettes made as in Test 1, from a briquetting mixture containing 7% of pitch with no oil addition, were weak and possessed such a low resistance to abrasion that great care had to be taken in their handling to avoid degradation. Tests 2 and 3 show the considerable increase in strength which was obtained when the coal was first sprayed with an oil before blending with the pitch. The improvement in quality was such that it was possible to transport the briquettes, made in Test 2, a considerable distance by road and to charge them to a full-scale carbonizing oven with only insignificant breakage.

HOT BRIQUETTING

By D. H. GREGORY

Coal Research Establishment, National Coal Board, Great Britain

Summary—In the manufacture of carbonized briquettes it is often necessary to pretreat the coal thermally before briquetting. The briquetting stage is then interposed between two heat treatments. To improve the overall thermal efficiency of such a process it is necessary to briquette at or near the temperature of the pretreatment stage.

By the addition of a fluxing agent, such as coal tar pitch, a wide range of coals has been made to soften sufficiently before decomposition to permit autoagglomeration of the fluxed coal. Thus, in a process involving a thermal oxidation pretreatment stage, coal has been autoagglomerated in the presence of a nominal 3% to 4% of pitch flux at temperatures about 300°C in a constant-volume double-roll press developing pressures up to 2 ton/sq. in.

In another process in which the coal was carbonized as a pretreatment, coal fluxed with pitch was used as a high-temperature-setting binder for the semicoke, at briquetting temperatures of 400°C to 440°C. The binder content required depended on the degree of carbonization of the semicoke, the ratio of coal to pitch and the nature of the coal in the binder.

In both these processes the briquettes were strong enough for mechanical transfer to the carbonizing unit immediately after manufacture, and they were carbonized satisfactorily provided the briquette temperature did not fall appreciably during the transfer.

Résumé—Dans la fabrication des agglomérés carbonisés il est souvent nécessaire de soumettre le charbon à un traitement thermique précédant l'agglomération. L'étape de l'agglomération est intercalés entre deux traitements thermiques. Afin d'améliorer le rendement thermique global d'un tel procédé, il est nécessaire d'agglomérer à la température de la phase du traitement préalable ou à une température voisine.

En ajoutant un réactif dans le mélange tel que du brai de goudron de houille, on a rendu toute une grande série de charbons apte à se ramollir suffisamment avant la décomposition pour permettre l'autoagglomération du charbon ainsi traité. C'est ainsi que dans un procédé comportant une phase de traitement préalable d'oxydation, le charbon a été autoaggloméré en présence de 3 à 4% de brai comme réactif à des températures d'environ 300°C dans une presse à volume constant à double cylindre donnant des pressions allant jusqu 'à 2 tonnes/pouce carré (310 kg/cm²).

Dans un autre procédé dans lequel le charbon était soumis au cours d'un traitement préalable à une carbonisation, du charbon, mélangé avec du brai comme réactif, était utilisé en guise de liant prenant à haute température pour le semi-coke, à des températures d'agglomération de 400 à 440°C. La teneur de liant nécessaire dépendait du degré de carbonisation du semi-coke, de la proportion du charbon au brai et de la nature du charbon du liant.

Dans ces deux procédés les agglomérés étaient assez résistants pour pouvoir supporter leur transport à l'appareil de carbonisation aussitôt après leur fabrication, ils étaient carbonisés d'une façon satisfaisante, pourvu que la température des agglomérés ne baissât pas d'une façon appréciable pendant ce transport.

Zusammenfassung—Die Herstellung von Schwelbriketts macht oftmals eine thermische Vorbehandlung der Kohle erforderlich, so dass der Brikettiervorgang zwischen die beiden Stufen der thermischen Behandlung eingeschaltet wird. Um den Gesamtwärmewirkungsgrad eines derartigen Verfahrens zu erhöhen, muss die Brikettierung bei der Temperatur der Vorbehandlung oder bei nur unwesentlich geringeren Wärmegraden vor sich gehen.

Durch Zusatz eines Flussmittels, beispielsweise Steinkohlenteerpech, gelang es, eine ziemlich weite Spanne von Kohlen vor Eintritt der Zersetzung so weit plastisch zu machen, dass sie sich brikettieren liessen. Es wurde in einem Verfahren eine Kohle nach Vorerwärmung und Oxydation und nach Zusatz von 3 bis 4% Pech als Flussmittel bei Temperaturen von etwa 300°C in einer Doppelwalzenpresse mit gleichbleibendem Volumen unter einem Druck bis zu rd. 310 kg/cm² brikettiert.

In einem anderen Verfahren wurde die Kohle zunächst vorgeschwelt; als Bindemittel für die bei Temperaturen von 400 bis 440°C erfolgende Brikettierung wurde dem angeschwelten Material eine Kohle beigegeben, der Pech als Flussmittel zugesetzt war. Der Bedarf an Bindemittel war abhängig von dem Grad der Vorschwelung der Ausgangskohle, von dem Verhältnis von Kohle zu Pech im Bindemittel und schliesslich von der Art der als Bindemittel verwendeten Kohle.

PLATE 1—BRIQUETTING OF OXIDIZED COAL

×180

A: Section of briquette made at conventional temperature (80°C): nonfused structure

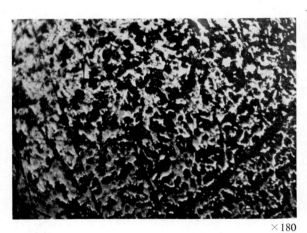

×180

B: Section of briquette made at high temperature (325°C): fused structure

PLATE 2A—INTERNAL STRUCTURE OF BINLEY COAL AND CHARS

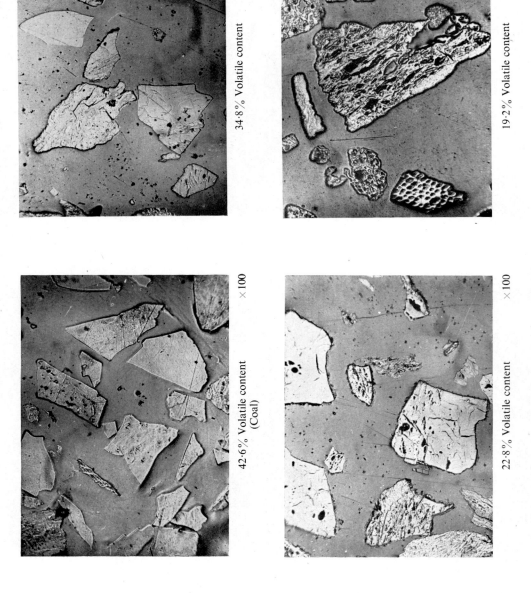

42·6% Volatile content
(Coal)   ×100

34·8% Volatile content   ×100

22·8% Volatile content   ×100

19·2% Volatile content   ×100

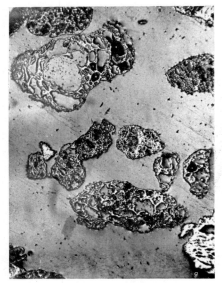

12·8% Volatile content   ×100

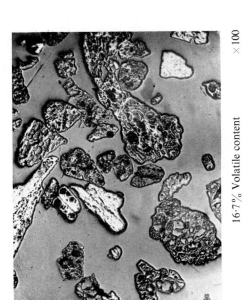

16·7% Volatile content   ×100

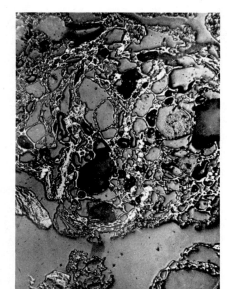

8·9% Volatile content   ×100

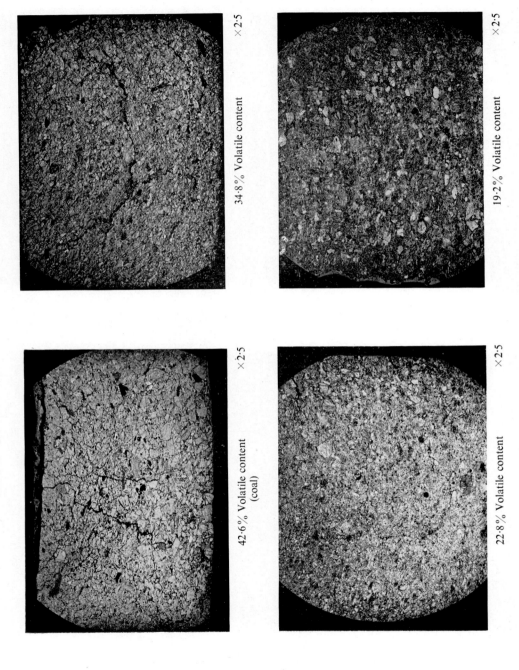

PLATE 2B—SECTIONS OF BINLEY COAL AND CHAR BRIQUETTES: UNCARBONIZED

42·6% Volatile content (coal)   ×2·5

34·8% Volatile content   ×2·5

22·8% Volatile content   ×2·5

19·2% Volatile content   ×2·5

16·7% Volatile content ×2·5

12·8% Volatile content ×2·5

8·9% Volatile content ×2·5

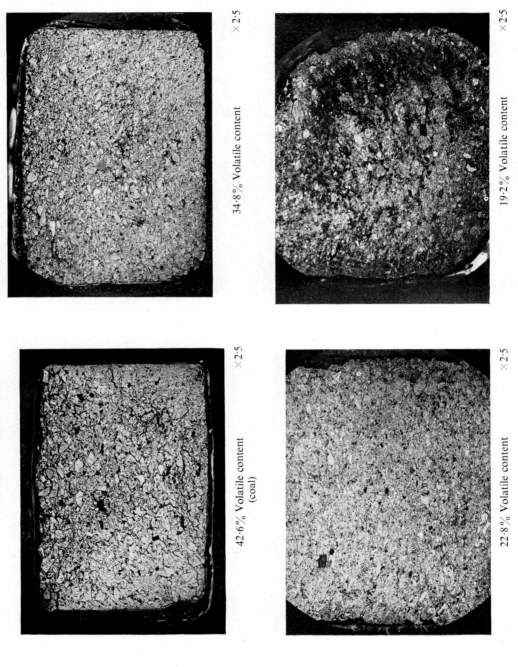

PLATE 2C—SECTION OF BINLEY COAL AND CHAR BRIQUETTES: CARBONIZED

42·6% Volatile content (coal)   ×2·5

34·8% Volatile content   ×2·5

22·8% Volatile content   ×2·5

19·2% Volatile content   ×2·5

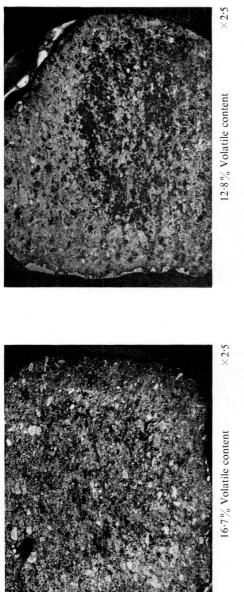

16·7% Volatile content   ×2·5

12·8% Volatile content   ×2·5

8·9% Volatile content   ×2·5

PLATE 2D—SURFACE CHARACTERISTICS OF BINLEY COAL AND CHARS

34·8% Volatile content

×5

19·2% Volatile content

×5

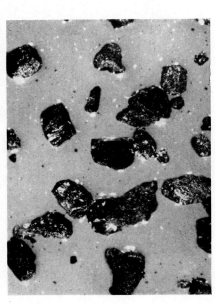

42·6% Volatile content
(coal)

×5

22·8% Volatile content

×5

16·7% Volatile content ×5

12·8% Volatile content ×5

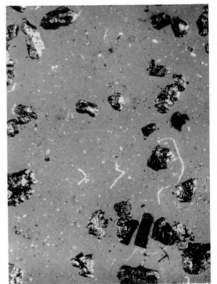

8·9% Volatile content ×5

Bei beiden Verfahren waren die erzeugten Briketts so fest, dass sie unmittelbar aus der Presse in den Schwelofen gehen konnten; auch die Schwelung verlief einwandfrei, sofern die Temperatur der Briketts auf dem Weg von der Presse in den Ofen nicht zu stark abfiel.

INTRODUCTION

ONE of the most important methods of producing a smokeless fuel to satisfy the increasing demand in this country involves briquetting of the coal and subsequent carbonization of the briquettes. A simple process comprising these two treatments only is applicable to a very limited number of British coals. In developing processes to utilize a wider range of coals it is necessary to pretreat the coals.

Many coals can be processed in this manner if they are first subjected to mild oxidation or to partial carbonization. In both these pretreatments the coal is heated to temperatures varying from approximately 300°C to 600°C so that the briquetting stage is interposed between two heat treatments, namely, the oxidation or carbonization pretreatment at temperatures between 300°C and 600°C and briquette carbonization at usually over 650°C.

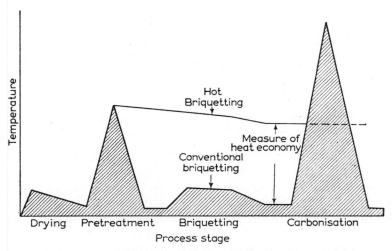

FIG. 1—Process temperature levels for conventional and hot briquetting.

If conventional briquetting, using coal-tar pitch as the binder, follows the pretreatment stage, the coal must be cooled to about 80°C; after briquetting, the briquettes must be cooled to near ambient temperatures to permit the pitch to set and impart sufficient strength to the briquettes for mechanical handling to the final carbonizing unit. In this last stage the briquettes have to be reheated through the temperature range of cooling of both the pretreated coal and the briquettes. The overall thermal efficiency of such a process, in which the sensible heat of the pretreatment is wasted, is obviously low. It can be considerably improved, however, as is illustrated in Fig. 1, if the briquetting operation is done at or near the pretreatment temperature provided the briquettes are sufficiently strong at these temperatures to withstand handling to the subsequent carbonization stage.

HOT-BRIQUETTING PROCESSES

It is essential that the briquettes, manufactured at the comparatively high temperatures of the oxidation or devolatilization processes, should possess sufficient strength at these temperatures for subsequent mechanical handling. The conventional binders are only effective after they harden and, since their " hardening " or " setting " temperatures are below 100°C, they are too fluid above 300°C to contribute to the strength of briquettes made at these temperatures. Other binders, therefore, with high " setting " temperatures had to be prepared if briquetting with a binder was to be employed.

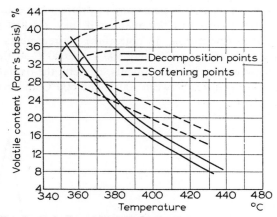

FIG. 2—Volatile content of coal in relation to the softening and decomposition temperatures (Based on data by J. B. Bennett, J. Inst. Fuel, **14**, 175, (1941).)

Hardy[1] and many other workers have shown that fine coal could be agglomerated without a binder to form briquettes if the coal was first heated so that it became plastic and then compressed. Darmont[2] has demonstrated that this plastic coal could be used as the binder for coke.

Unfortunately, however, only a comparatively small group of coals soften before they decompose, and, as gas evolution during compression must be severely limited in briquetting, the temperature range between softening and decomposition for even this small group of coals is too narrow for successful briquette manufacture. Indeed, development of this process has been confined to one 5-ton-per-hour unit.[3]

Bennett,[4] referring to the coal softening curves of Seyler and the decomposition temperatures of Evans, has indicated that, with low rates of heating, only those coals of 24% to 34% volatile content (Parr's Basis) soften before decomposition—see Fig. 2. Moreover, even with these coals the maximum difference in temperature between the softening and decomposition points was of the order of 10°C only. It was known that an increased rate of heating had a marked effect in lowering the temperature at which the coal softened and in raising its decomposition temperature. With rapid heating, therefore, it was expected that both the range of coals which softened before decomposition and the softening zone before decomposition would be widened, but even under these conditions Darmont[2] has stated that only fusible coals could be considered suitable for a process of briquetting at high temperatures.

C.R.E. HOT-BRIQUETTING METHOD

Recent and indeed current work at the Coal Research Establishment of the National Coal Board has indicated that the practical difficulties of briquetting within the plastic range of the coal may be overcome by the addition of a fluxing agent, such as coal-tar pitch, to the coal. The object of the flux addition is to make the coal more fusible over a wider temperature range. Fig. 3 shows the relationships between the softening temperatures by the Gieseler method and pitch flux contents for four

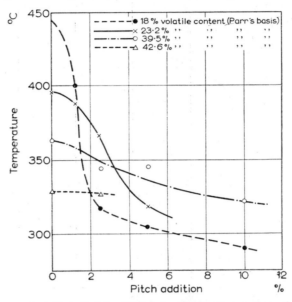

Fig. 3—Effect of pitch addition on softening temperature of
pitch and coal mixture—Gieseler method.

coals varying in volatile content from 18% to 42·6% (Parr's Basis). The rate of heating employed in these tests was 10°C/min which, although well below that which would be employed in hot-briquetting practice, was the maximum attainable in the Gieseler apparatus used.

It will be noted in Fig. 3 that, for the coal of 18% volatile content, pitch additions up to 4% had a considerable effect, lowering the initial softening temperature from 443°C without pitch to 330°C with 2% pitch and to 310°C with 4% pitch. Further increases in the amount of pitch did not cause the same remarkable changes in temperature of softening. As the volatile contents of these four coals increased, the effect of the flux additions on the softening points became less marked; thus with the coal of 23·2% volatile content, the pertinent temperatures were 395°C without pitch, 375°C with a 2% addition and 332°C with 4%. With the coal of 39·5% volatile content the temperatures were 367°C without pitch, 350°C with 2% addition and 340°C with 4%. Only with the coal of highest volatile content (42·6%) was there no response to the addition of pitch.

The limited number of coals so far examined in this way has shown that the range of coals which could be made to soften before decomposing was extended to those with a volatile content of at least 18% to 39·5%. Since experimental work has shown that the addition of the pitch does not alter the decomposition temperature of the coal, the permissible briquetting temperature range of all the coals examined was increased. For example, the temperature range for the 18% volatile content coal was increased by 110°C when 2% pitch was present and by 130°C when 4% of pitch was used as the flux.

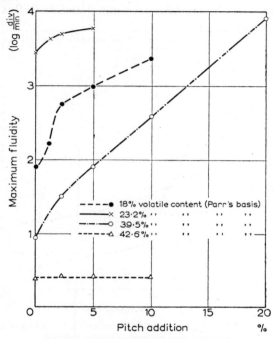

Fig. 4—Effect of pitch addition on maximum fluidity of pitch and coal mixture—Gieseler method.

Apart from lowering the temperature at which the three coals softened, the addition of the flux also considerably increased the degree of fluidity, as is shown in Fig. 4. Again the effect was most marked with the initial additions of the pitch flux, with a decrease in the potency of subsequent increments. It was interesting to note that the fluidity of coals which cannot be regarded as fusible, e.g. those of 18% and 39·5% volatile content, was increased by the addition of pitch to that of a coal which may be classified as fusible, e.g. one of 23·2% volatile content.

The effects of introducing the flux were, therefore, that the range of coals which soften before decomposition was widened and that the permissible briquetting temperature range was increased.

APPLICATION OF HOT BRIQUETTING OF FLUXED COAL

Two processes in which advantage is taken of the fluxing effect of coal-tar pitch on coal are being developed at the Coal Research Establishment. In the first, coal which has been thermally oxidized is autoagglomerated at or near the oxidation temperature in the presence of the flux, whilst in the second the increased fluidity of the coal engendered by the addition of pitch is an important factor in its use as a binder for char.

1. *Briquetting of Oxidized Coal*

In another paper to this Conference, a process is described in which low-volatile but highly swelling coal is thermally oxidized before briquetting in order to control the subsequent carbonization behaviour of the briquettes. The briquetting stage in this process is interposed between two stages of heat treatment, namely oxidation at temperatures between 300°C and 400°C and briquette carbonization at temperatures of over 650°C.

a) Briquetting variables. Briquetting experiments on both a small batch and a continuous scale have shown that the important variables in the hot briquetting of oxidized coal were (*a*) the degree of oxidation of the coal, (*b*) the amount of pitch flux added and (*c*) the temperature of briquetting. (The size grading of the coal was not considered as a variable in these experiments since it was determined by the oxidation treatment.)

As expected, these three important variables were closely interrelated. As the degree of oxidation became more severe, both the required flux content and the minimum briquetting temperature increased. Furthermore, with samples which had been oxidized to a desired level, the amount of flux required for satisfactory briquetting tended to decrease with increasing briquetting temperature. On the small continuous experimental plant scale, however, the optimum conditions, derived from tests in which the coal was oxidized at 350°C and the briquettes subsequently carbonized, were a briquetting temperature of about 325°C and a nominal flux addition of 3% to 4%. The flux addition is given as a nominal one because, during the mixing of the flux with the coal, a certain amount was driven off as volatile. Under the optimum conditions the volatile loss attributed to the pitch was 30% of the original addition— the actual flux content of the briquette, therefore, was approximately 2% to 3%. Under the conditions of oxidation used, the agglutinating value of the coal, employed as a measure of the degree of oxidation, was reduced from about 13 to between 1 and 4. The oxidized coal processed in these tests did not exhibit any softening in the Gieseler apparatus except in the presence of 4% pitch when a softening temperature of 350°C was noted. Even so, as shown in Plate 1, polished sections of briquettes made under the optimum conditions revealed considerable fusion of the particles.

b) Type of press. Both Thau[3] and Darmont[2] considered that constant volume presses could not be employed for hot briquetting. However, laboratory batch experiments with fluxed coal indicated that the variation in briquette strength with pressure was no greater than in conventional briquetting with pitch as a binder. Confirmation of this relationship was obtained in experiments in a small continuous unit in which a double-roll press, i.e. a constant-volume press, was included. It appeared, therefore, at least with the unit employed, that if the coal is fluxed, constant-volume presses of the double-roll type with all their advantages could be used for hot briquetting. The results of the experimental plant tests also suggested that special heat-resisting steels are not required since the equilibrium temperature of the rolls was between 150°C and 170°C when the temperature of the coal at the point of compression varied between 300°C and 325°C. Little advantage was gained by artificially heating the rolls to the briquetting temperature.

  c) Cooling characteristics. The cooling characteristics of the briquettes varied with the size and shape of the product. In all cases, however, as is shown in Fig. 5, the onset of strength was much more rapid when the briquettes were manufactured

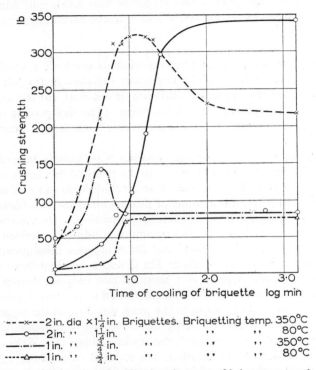

·---×---2 in. dia ×1¼ in. Briquettes. Briquetting temp. 350°C
——○——2 in. ,,   1¼ in.   ,,   ,,   ,,   80°C
—·—·—1 in. ,,   ¾ in.   ,,   ,,   ,,   350°C
----△----1 in. ,,   ¾ in.   ,,   ,,   ,,   80°C

FIG. 5—Briquetting of oxidized coal—onset of briquette strength.

by this fluxing method than when they were made under conventional conditions with pitch as a binder. As Fig. 5 shows, there was a characteristic peak strength of the briquettes made at temperatures above 300°C, the prominence of the peak increasing with rising briquetting temperature. The decrease in the briquette strength on cooling beyond the peak-strength period was attributed to two causes, (*a*) internal stresses, caused by a too rapid and, therefore, unequal cooling, and (*b*) different thermal contractions of the petrographic constituents of the original coal. Both causes were considered to be important but the only one which could be modified practically was the rate of cooling. If a continuous unit were used for the carboniza-tion of the briquettes, then there is no problem of their cooling. In this case, since the briquettes would be sufficiently strong for mechanical handling immediately after manufacture, they preferably would be charged into the carbonizing oven before the peak strength was attained. If, however, the briquettes were allowed to cool in air to below the temperature at which the peak strength occurred as for example they may be in batch carbonization, then the carbonized product would be of low strength owing to the expansion of hair cracks which appeared in the green briquettes. Batch carbonization, however, could be employed without causing an appreciable reduction in the strength of the carbonized product, as is shown in Fig. 6,

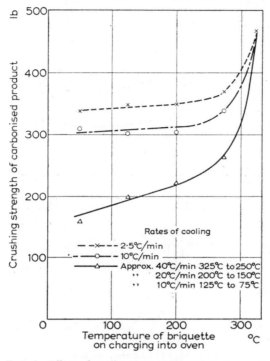

FIG. 6—Effect of cooling green briquettes before carbonization on strength of product.

if the rate of cooling of the briquettes were controlled to less than 10°C/min, particularly in the temperature range of 325°C to about 200°C, even though the final temperature was reduced to that of the atmosphere.

2. *Briquetting of Semicoke or Char*

The hot-briquetting technique has been applied to another three-stage process being developed at CRE. In this process again the briquetting stage is interposed between two heat-treatment stages, the first being partial carbonization of the coal at temperatures between 400°C and 650°C to produce a semicoke or char, the second carbonization of the briquettes at temperatures above 650°C. In this process the degree of initial carbonization was such that the inherent fluidity of the original coal was reduced or destroyed and no reasonable addition of a flux would induce sufficient softening of the char for briquetting. The method adopted, therefore, was to employ for the char a binder consisting of coal and a flux such as pitch. These two components (that is, coal and pitch) when mixed in the proportions employed in this work acted as a high-temperature-setting binder. The action of the pitch in lowering the minimum briquetting temperature and widening the permissible briquetting temperature range is well demonstrated in Fig. 7. In both diagrams it can be seen that with a char and compound binder mixture containing 5% pitch, the briquetting temperature range was at least twice that permissible when coal alone was used.

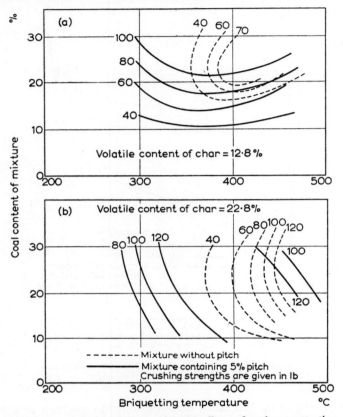

FIG. 7—Iso-strength curves showing the effects of coal concentration, briquetting temperature and addition of pitch.

a) Briquetting variables. Although, as yet, this briquetting method has been developed only on a laboratory scale, the variables which affect the strength of both the green and carbonized briquettes have been determined. These variables were the volatile content of the semicoke or char, the composition of the coal and flux compound binder, the compound binder content, the type of coal employed in the compound binder and the temperature of briquetting.

b) Properties of the chars. One of the most important variables for the series of chars examined was the volatile content of the char, since this value could be related to the structure, shape and indeed size grading of the particles. It is well known in conventional processes of briquetting that these three factors govern, to a large extent, the binder requirements and strength of the briquettes.

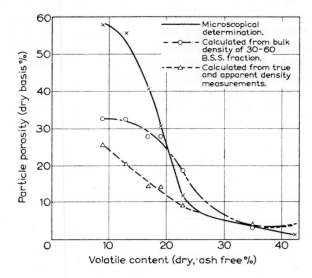

Fig. 8—Relation between porosity and volatile content of Binley chars.

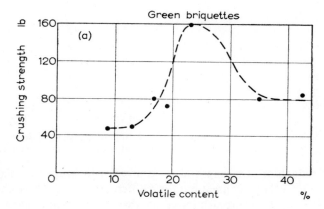

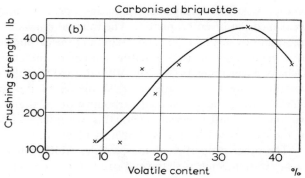

Fig. 9—Crushing strength of briquettes produced from chars of varying volatile content. (Binder content 14% (9·8% coal, 4·2% pitch); briquetting temperature 420°C).

E

A microscopical examination of the chars of various volatile contents revealed that, as the carbonization became more drastic, the particles developed a porous structure and at the lowest volatile content the pore size was extremely large—see Plate 2A. The porosity of the chars did not alter appreciably down to the 25% volatile content level (see Fig. 8), but thereafter it increased markedly with decreasing volatile content. It was not surprising, therefore, that the briquettes produced from the chars of less than 25% volatile content under standard conditions of binder composition and content, and of briquetting temperature and pressure, were not as strong as those made from chars of approximately 25% volatile content—see Fig. 9(a). This

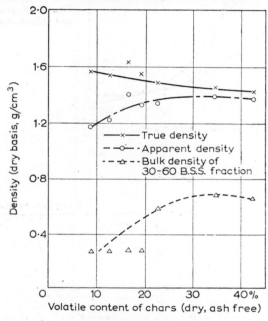

FIG. 10—True, apparent and bulk densities of Binley
chars at various volatile contents.

reduction of strength also occurred with briquettes made from chars of more than 30% volatile content but for a different reason. These chars of higher volatile content, having been precarbonized at lower temperatures than the briquetting temperature, emitted volatiles during the briquetting operation and these produced cracks which weakened the green briquettes. The internal cracks are shown clearly in the first two photographs of Plate 2B. The strength of the carbonized briquettes, see Fig. 9(b), was at a maximum when the volatile content of the char was between 30% and 35%. Density measurements (see Fig. 10) indicated that the char was most compact at this volatile content level; therefore, shrinkage of the char away from the compound binder during the subsequent carbonization of the briquettes was minimized. Even without the density measurements this was inferred from the photographs of sections of the carbonized briquette shown in Plate 2C.

The other properties of the particles which can be related to the degree of pre-carbonization, such as shape and size grading, of course, contributed to the maximum

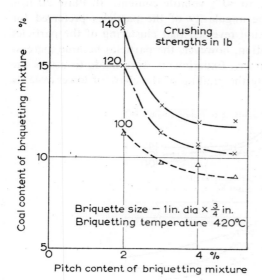

FIG. 11—Effect of coal and pitch concentration on briquette strength: iso-strength curves for 22·8% volatile content char.

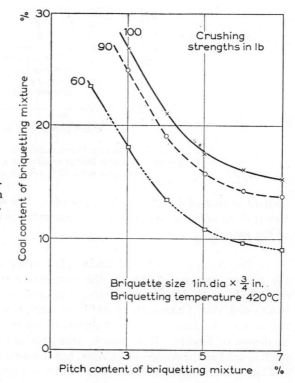

FIG. 12—Effect of coal and pitch concentration briquette strength: iso-strength curves for 12·8% volatile content char.

strength obtained with the chars of 25% to 30% volatile content. In Plate 2D it is shown that these chars still retained the angularity of the particles preferred for briquetting, and a size grading examination revealed that clustering of the particles had not occurred. On further carbonization, however, the particles became increasingly spherical and the size grading coarser. Experiments were made to assess the effect of varying size grading by adjusting the grading of the chars of lower volatile

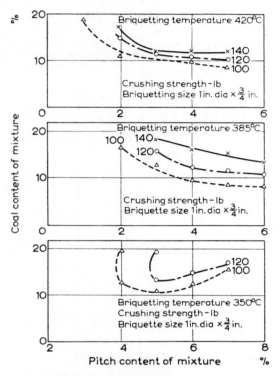

FIG. 13—Briquette Iso-strength curves relating binder composition with binder content at various briquetting temperatures for a 22% volatile content char.

content to that of the 25% to 30% samples. The results, however, indicated that the size-grading variation was of minor importance compared with the porosity and shape of the particles.

c) *Properties of compound binder.* The other variables, such as composition of the binder, amount of binder, the briquetting temperature and the type of coal employed in the binder, were closely related to each other. It has already been mentioned that Darmont's work[2] has indicated that, when using coal alone as the binder, the amount required depended upon the type of coal employed, i.e. on its degree of fluidity. This must be true also to some extent when coal fluxed with pitch is used as the compound binder, but it would appear from the results illustrated in Figs. 3 and 4 that the amount of binder required depended on the fluidity of the coal and pitch mixture rather than on that of the coal itself. For example, when three coals, having maximum fluidities of 1010 divs/min, 10,000 divs/min, and 1040 divs/min determined by the Gieseler method, were used with pitch as the compound binder, the required binder content under standard conditions of briquetting was 14%, 16% and 20% respectively. Thus, in spite of the very high inherent fluidity of the second coal compared with the other two, the binder contents were similar.

In general, the coal to pitch ratio in the compound binder could be varied over a

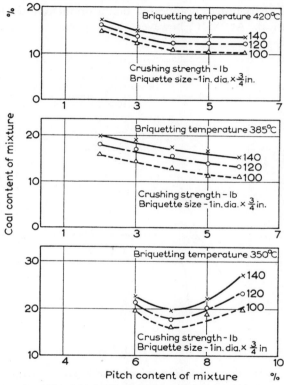

FIG. 14—Briquette Iso-strength curves relating binder composition with binder content at various briquetting temperatures for a 16% volatile content char.

wide range, provided the binder content was suitably adjusted. A typical example of the relationship between the constituents of the compound binder is shown in Figs. 11 and 12. These isostrength curves show, for example, that, with the char of 22·8% volatile content, to obtain a briquette with a crushing strength of 100 lb. the proportion of coal by weight of the total mixture could vary from 9·8% to 11·2% if the nominal pitch content was also varied from 5% to 2%, i.e. the coal to pitch ratio could be altered from about 2 to 1 to approximately 6 to 1. The change in total compound binder requirement with this alteration in coal to pitch ratio varied from 13% to 15%. In order to achieve a similar briquette strength with the char of 12·8% volatile content, the coal content of the total mixture varied from 25% to 15%

if the pitch content was increased from 3·5% to 7·5%, i.e. from a coal to pitch ratio of 7 to 1 to a ratio of 2 to 1. With this change in composition the total binder content was reduced from 28·5% to 22·5%. It must be noted that the pitch contents given are nominal figures since an appreciable loss of this binder component resulted when the compound binder was heated with the char.

The interrelationship between binder content, binder composition and briquetting temperature is well illustrated in Figs. 13 and 14. The type of coal employed as the major constituent in the binder was unchanged in these experiments. With the restricted range of chars tested, it appeared that a briquetting temperature of 350°C was somewhat critical. At 385°C, however, there appeared to be no difficulties and

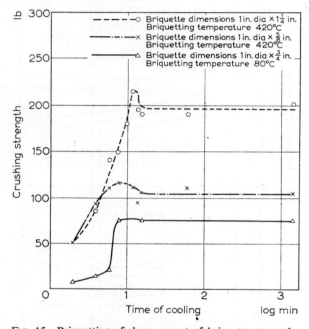

FIG. 15—Briquetting of chars—onset of briquette strength.

the binder requirements when briquetting at this temperature were only 1½% to 3% higher than those at 420°C. These temperature conditions have been determined on a laboratory scale where the char and the coal and pitch binder were heated together at a maximum rate of 40°C/min. It is not unreasonable to suppose that with much more rapid heating of the binder on a plant scale, when the sensible heat of the hot char can be used to accomplish the heating, a wider range of briquetting temperature will be permissible as well as a more favourable binder composition and binder content.

d) Type of press. The effect of briquetting pressure on the strength of the briquettes has been examined. These experiments indicated that the variation in briquette strength with pressure was no greater than in conventional briquetting with pitch alone as the binder. Although this conclusion has not yet been confirmed on a continuous scale, it would appear that constant-volume presses of the double-roll type, with all their advantages, could be used for the hot briquetting of chars.

e) Cooling characteristics. The cooling characteristics of the briquettes varied with the size and shape of the product as with those made from oxidized coal. The incorporation of the inert semi coke in the briquette, however, resulted in a more gradual and less marked reduction in strength after the peak was reached as is shown

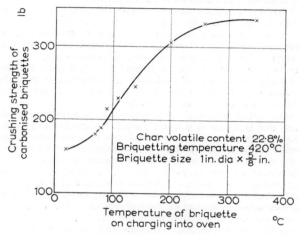

Fig. 16—Effect of cooling green briquettes before carbonization on strength of product.

in Fig. 15. However, carbonization tests on the briquettes indicated that it was again preferable to charge the briquettes into the carbonizing oven before the peak was reached in order to conserve the heat and to obtain a carbonized product of high strength. This is shown clearly in Fig. 16.

CONCLUSION

This survey of hot briquetting processes under development at CRE is essentially a preliminary one. The results so far obtained indicate however that, by the introduction of a flux, briquetting at elevated temperatures may now be feasible commercially.

Acknowledgements—The author is greatly indebted to his colleagues in the Briquetting Department at CRE both for their able execution of the work described in this paper and for their material help in preparing the paper itself.

REFERENCES

1. HARDY H., *Belg. Pat.* 399, 159 (1933).
2. DARMONT G., *Fuel* **31**, 75 (1952).
3. THAU A., *Colliery Guard* **149**, 333, 383 (1934).
4. BENNETT J. G., *J. Inst. Fuel* **14**, 175 (1941).

DISCUSSION

IR. G. KARDAUN (*Staatsmijnen in Limburg, Geleen*):

In the last few years we in the Netherlands have been working on the manufacture of a smokeless fuel from fine coal. After studying the existing production methods we first chose the well-known Phurnacite process. In 1953 we started production of 100 tons a day in a pilot plant. So far, this plant has operated to our full satisfaction. Our results are similar to those obtained in the British plant.

We found just what has been reported here, that the nature of the coal used is a very important factor. As soon as the volatile matter of the coal rises above 12%, serious difficulties are encountered, such as deformation, cracking, and clustering of the briquettes.

We are convinced that it is technically possible to make this coal, which has a higher percentage of volatile matter, suitable for the process by subjecting it to preliminary oxidation or degasification. We wonder however, whether the total costs of pretreatment, briquetting and carbonization would not render the process uneconomic. We therefore started research to use coal as a binder in order to make the after-treatment of the briquettes by carbonization unnecessary.

We have taken up the suggestion advanced by Dunkel (Silesia) in 1926. He states that for briquetting different types of coal no binder need be used when the coal is heated up to about 400°C, because at this temperature these coals soften. Low-volatile coal which will not soften by itself may be briquetted by the addition of a melting coal as a binder.

The process has been studied by several investigators, e.g. by Swietoslawski and Roga in Silesia, Levy in France, Hardy and Darmont in Belgium, Jappelt in Germany and the National Coal Board in Great Britain. However, production on a technical scale does not seem to have been realized.

We found a solution to the difficult problem of the technical realization of a rapid and homogeneous heating of the coal with an accuracy of a few degrees centigrade. In our case we want to briquette low-volatile coal with a melting coal as a binder. Overheating of this low-volatile coal does not have any harmful consequences. The coal is heated up to the degree needed to bring the temperature of the binder coal, which is supplied afterwards, to the required level. The problem of mixing the two components has been solved by feeding the binding coal into a dispersion of the hot coal in a fast current of gas. The instantaneous mixing achieved in this way, together with the fact that the starting temperature is not very high and that the heat is transmitted by the gas phase, rules out any danger of local overheating of the fines with the binding properties, while at the same time these fines are heated up very rapidly.

We have tried this process with various coals. The results obtained are favourable. As regards hardness and abrasion resistance, the uncarbonized briquettes are of the same quality as good pitch-bound briquettes. However, they produce much less smoke. In this respect, and also as regards their burning properties, they may be compared with good quality low-volatile nuts (10% v.m.). We even found it possible to use very poorly caking coals (14% v.m.) as a binding agent. Owing to the very high heating rate (only seconds), this coal is also completely softened, as can be clearly seen under the microscope. If still desired, briquettes made in this way can be submitted to a mild and rapid thermal after-treatment which has a highly beneficial effect on their hardness. Our experimental work in this field was started in 1952 and was largely carried out in a 1 ton-per-hour pilot plant. We do not yet consider it to be completed.

I would like to ask Mr. Gregory, if you here in Stoke Orchard are also studying hot-briquetting processes without using any pitch at all?

AUTHOR:

I am very much interested to hear of Mr. Kardaun's experiments on high-temperature briquetting of low-volatile coals using coal as a binder. In addition to briquetting chars we have also briquetted anthracite with a fluxed coal binder. We have preferred, however, to use a fluxed coal rather than coal alone because we believe the briquetting operation is thereby simplified. A wider briquetting temperature range is permissible and, it would appear from Mr. Kardaun's remarks, the pressing operation itself is simplified since we have been able to use a constant-volume double-roll press with all its advantages.

In the first instance, we considered these high-temperature briquetting processes as an intermediate stage between two heat treatment stages, i.e. the final product was a carbonized briquette. However, the green briquettes are sufficiently smokeless for us to consider the elimination of the final carbonization treatment when the fuel is intended for open grates.

With regard to Mr. Kardaun's question on briquetting without a binder, unfortunately I cannot add anything to that already published.

MR. E. P. MILLS (*National Coal Board, Stoke Orchard*):

Mr. Gregory has noted that adding pitch to coal can, in certain instances, bring about considerable lowering of the initial softening temperature and increase the degree of fluidity. However, no figures are produced to demonstrate the effect of pitch addition on the actual briquettability. Has the author any information on this point?

The method described involves adding coal and pitch to hot char. Would there be any advantage in preparing the compound binder by heating the coal and pitch together before adding it to the char?

AUTHOR:

In Fig. 7 of my paper I have shown how the addition of a pitch flux to the coal increases the permissible temperature range of briquetting compared with the restricted range available when coal is the sole binder constituent. But Mr. Mills is, perhaps, referring to the desirable fluidity of the coal when the fluxed coal is briquetted alone. From the work we have done it does appear that the coal can be over-plasticized. This means that the larger the quantity of pitch flux added to the coal the lower will be the optimum temperature of briquetting, since if the temperature is too high, weak briquettes are produced. The optimum briquetting temperatures lie within 10°C or so of the initial softening point of the mixture in the Gieseler apparatus.

Of course, this does not apply to the briquetting of chars where as high a degree of fluidity of the binder as possible is desirable.

MR. W. N. ADAMS (*National Coal Board, Stoke Orchard*):

Fig. 8 in Mr. Gregory's paper relates the volatile content of the char to the briquette strength, but obviously it is not the property of the char which is related directly to the strength of the briquette since semicokes of the same volatile content but produced by different methods have different structures. These differences have been discussed in the paper presented at this Conference by Messieurs Foch and Peytavy. The differences have been observed also by Price and Woody in America.*

What does the author consider to be the property of a char which does affect the "briquettability"? Is it plasticity, porosity, or cell-wall strength, to name a few likely properties? Alternatively, would a better parameter be the plasticity characteristics of the semicoke-coal-pitch mixture?

AUTHOR:

This question is, of course, a very important one and to do it justice would require a long discussion. As Mr. Adams has said the volatile content is not the property of the char which is related directly to the strength of the briquettes.

I think we must begin by eliminating one variable which is of paramount importance. That is, the relation between the coal carbonization temperature and the briquetting temperature. If the briquetting temperature is similar to or higher than the carbonization temperature the briquettes will not be sound since internal cracks caused by the emission of volatile matter will weaken them. This is clearly shown in Fig. 2(*b*). Assuming we do not have this trouble let us consider the surface characteristics which may affect the briquetting qualities of the chars. Plate 2D shows that high briquetting strengths are associated with angular particles. This is also true in conventional briquetting. When the particles become more spherical the briquettes become weaker under the standard conditions of briquetting. There are, of course, other surface characteristics such as rugosity and surface wettability of the chars to be considered because these also must affect the briquettability. Briquetting characteristics will also be affected to some degree by the size grading and particle strength.

As stated in the paper, however, the porosity also plays an important part. In fact, with chars made under various conditions from one coal we have shown that porosity seems to be one of the most, if not the most, important factor in determining the briquettability of the chars. In Fig. 8 we have plotted the porosity of the chars determined by several methods against the volatile content of the chars. You will notice that the porosity increases markedly at about 25% volatile content.

We have also constructed a curve for porosity versus crushing strength for chars made under specific conditions and have used this curve as a basic line. Data for chars made under different conditions but as yet with only one coal have been plotted on this graph. In the region of porosities up to 25% we have obtained good results in that the strength versus porosity relationship for these new chars more or less coincide with the original curve.

With regard to the last part of Mr. Adam's question, the plasticity characteristics of the mixture may be a better parameter. In view of all the other characteristics which also play a part in determining the briquettability of the char there may be some doubt about the value of plasticity measurements but I do agree that it would be a worthwhile investigation.

---

* PRICE J. D. and WOODY G. V., *Trans. Amer. Inst. Min. Engrs.*, **157**, 317 (1944).

DR. J. BRONOWSKI (*National Coal Board, Stoke Orchard*):

The Conference will be interested to know that Monsieur Cheradame at the Fifth World Power Conference in Vienna last week, reported practical French work which takes advantage of the known fact that when some anthracene oils are added to pitch, the amount of pitch needed to act as a binder in briquetting is lowered. If any of our French colleagues here can make a fuller statement now about this work, it would fit very well to what Dr. Reerink and Mr. Launder have just said. If not, I will ask them for a written contribution on this point.

MONSIEUR A. F. BOYER (*Centre d'Études et Recherches des Charbonnages de France, Verneuil*):

During trials on briquetting, we observed that the wetting power of a pitch is higher, the lower the viscosity of this pitch at the mixing temperature. The requirements of grinding and handling the pitch are unfavourable to the use of a substance with an excessively low softening point. We have been able to overcome this difficulty by the following means: first of all the coal fines and the ground hard pitch are mixed, and—before the mixture reaches the stirrer—anthracene oil on tar is added to act as a flux to the binder. A saving in pitch results from this; one part of oil replaces approximately two parts of pitch. The quantity of oil which can be added is restricted by the conditions of handling the briquettes. A similar result is obtained if cracked-petroleum bitumen is used as a binder.

A STUDY OF SEMICARBONIZATION IN A FLUIDIZED BED*

By A. Peytavy and P. Foch

Centre d'Études et Recherches des Charbonnages de France, Marienau, France

Summary—Investigations carried out at Cerchar and at the experimental station at Marienau have two simultaneous objectives:

(1) An investigation of the phenomenon of fluidization and of its application to the semicarbonization of coal, including the behaviour of the coal, the quality of the products obtained and the establishment of material and thermal balanced sheets.

(2) A technological investigation with the intention of formulating a detailed specification for an industrial plant.

Although the problems differ in nature, they are so closely interconnected as to become inseparable in an industrial-scale investigation.

As a matter of urgency, the trials were first of all directed to the manufacture of a semicoke intended to replace coke dust; the latter is normally used in the coke blends which are charged in tamped coke ovens in the Saar-Lorraine district.

A number of industrial solutions were considered. The method selected was that making use of internal heating by means of partial combustion of the coal in the draught air. If the plant is, in addition, provided with a suitable preheater—to preheat both the coal and the air—the throughput rate can be increased, the quality of the gas improved (the calorific value being 2,500 kcal/m³ (250 B.t.u./lb.) and probably 3,000 kcal/m³ (300 B.t.u./lb.)); in addition it would be possible to reduce the proportion of coal burned to approximately 3%.

The trials were carried out in the first instance, on the 200 lb./hour scale and subsequently on the scale of 1 ton/hour; they made it possible to outline in principle the specification for an industrial plant with a throughput of 10 tons/hour. This plant is at present being developed.

Résumé—Les études exécutées au Cerchar et à la Station Experimentale de Marienau visent simultanément deux objectifs:

(1) Une étude du phénomène de la fluidisation et de son application à la semi-carbonisation du charbon, y compris le comportement des charbons, la qualité des produits obtonus et l'établissement de bilans matières et thermiques.

(2) Une étude technologique dont le but est de préciser les détails d'exécution d'une unite industrielle.

Bien que de nature différente, ces problèmes s'interpénêtrent tellement qu'ils sont inséparables dans une étude industrielle.

Les essais ont été orientés en première urgence vers la fabrication d'un semi-coke destiné à remplacer le poussier de coke qu'on doit incorporer dans les mélanges de charbons enfournés dans les cokeries pilonnées sarro-lorraines.

Plusieurs solutions industrielles ont été envisagées. On a retenu le chauffage interne par combustion partielle du charbon à l'air soufflé. Si l'on complète l'installation par un préchauffage convenable du charbon et de l'air, on peut augmenter l'allure, améliorer le gaz (2500 et probablement 3000 kcal/m³) et réduire la fraction de charbon brûlé (a environ 3%).

Les essais, conduits d'abord à l'échelle 100 kg/h puis à l'échelle 1 t/h ont permis de dégager les principes de construction d'une unité industrielle capable de 10 t/h dont l'étude est actuellement en cours.

Zusammenfassung—Mit den in den Laboratorien des Cerchar und in der Versuchsstation Marienau durchgeführhten Arbeiten wurden gleichzeitig zwei Ziele verfolgt:

(1) Klärung der Vorgänge im Wirbelbett und Anwendung dieses Verfahrens zur Schwelung von Kohle, Beobachtung des Verhaltens der verschiedenen Kohlen, Untersuchung der Erzeugnisse und Aufstellung von Stoff- und Wärmebilanzen.

* Work carried out by Cerchar(Centre d'Études et Recherches des Charbonnages de France). The execution of the tests themselves, together with an appreciable part of the study here reviewed and the evaluation of the results, was due to MM. Bosschem, Geoffrey, and Lahouste, engineers at Cerchar.

(2) Klärung der konstruktionellen Fragen, die der Bau einer Anlage in technischem Massstab mit sich bringt, und Ausarbeitung der Pläne hierfür.

Diese beiden Aufgaben sind zwar ihrem Wesen nach verschieden, andererseits jedoch eng miteinander verbunden und bei Forschungsarbeiten mot praktischer Zielsetzung nicht voneinander zu trennen.

Vordringlich dienten die Versuche der Herstellung eines Halbkokses als Ersatz für den Koksstaub, der bisher den gestampften Chargen der saarländischen und lothringischen Kokereien beigemischt werden muss.

Bei den Versuchen wurden verschiedenartige technische Lösungen erprobt. Man entschied sich schliesslich für Innenbeheizung bei teilweiser Verbrennung der Kohle in eingeblasener Luft. Bei Vorerwärmung von Kohle und Luft kann man die Durchsatzleistung steigern, die Qualität des Gases (auf 2500 und wahrscheinlich 3000 kcal/m³) verbessern und den Anteil der verbrannten Kohle (auf ungefähr 3%) senken.

Die Versuche wurden anfänglich mit einer Durchsatzleistung von 100 kg/h, dann von 1 t/h durchgeführt. Auf Grund der dabei gewonnenen Erfahrungen konnten die Richtlinien für den Bau einer Anlage im technischen Massstab (10 t/h) festgelegt werden; die Pläne werden zur Zeit in ihren Einzelheiten ausgearbeitet.

I. OBJECT OF THE INVESTIGATION

Semicarbonization of coal, that is to say, the carbonization of coal at low or medium temperatures* yields three principal products: semicoke, tar and gas. It is therefore possible to have very different objectives, according to whether the emphasis falls on one or another of these products.

So far as we are aware, no one has attempted to carry out semicarbonization with the prime object of obtaining gas. It has, in point of fact, been noted that the quantity of gas produced was not sufficiently large to justify applying the process with this end in view; moreover, the gas is frequently of inadequate quality. As against this, the tar or the semicoke can be considered, according to circumstances, to be a high-grade product. For example, a large installation has been constructed at Rockdale (U.S.A.) in order to recover the tars from high-volatile coals, before the coal is sent to the power station. In this case the valuable product is tar, the semicoke being a byproduct.

As far as we are concerned, it is the semicoke which is the principal product, since we are attempting to perfect an additive which is intended to improve the quality of the blends fed to coke ovens. We have several aims in this field and give a brief sketch of these below:

a) Although the Lorraine coals do not possess good coking characteristics they can be used in very large proportions (70% to 80%) in blends for blast-furnace coke, in conjunction with the tamping technique. This considerably improves the cohesion of the coke, but not the degree of fissuration. The latter can be modified effectively by incorporating in the blend suitably ground coke dust. Unfortunately, the coke ovens preparing this coke have not sufficient supplies of coke dust and must buy it elsewhere.

We have had occasion to show that semicoke produced by fluidization at a temperature of about 800°C has " antifissurant " properties comparable with those of coke dust and that it could, in consequence, be used to replace this.

---

* The expressions " low temperature ", " high temperature " are obviously conventional. These two terms refer respectively to carbonization carried out at temperatures of about 500°C and 1000°C. Medium-temperature carbonization would therefore be that carried out at temperatures of between 700°C and 800°C.

b) If tamping is not carried out, coals with a high volatile content yield a small, fragile coke which may, however, possess an acceptable degree of cohesion. It is sometimes possible to improve this coke by adding semicoke to the coals in the blend. Some few years ago we used for this purpose semicoke from a rotary furnace; it will be necessary to study this point again with semicoke produced by fluidization. The conditions of use may, perhaps, be different from those which obtained in the earlier case; it will therefore be necessary to investigate the question specially. It should, however, be pointed out that the cokes which can be obtained in this way are not good metallurgical cokes, but may be suitable for other industrial uses.

c) The semicoke is also used for the preparation of domestic coke from certain coals from the North of France. In the Carbolux process, which has been in use at Bruay for 25 years, a blend of coal and of semicoke from rotary ovens (15% volatile content) is charged in furnaces similar to coke ovens, but heated to a lower temperature. Here again, it is possible to envisage the use of semicoke produced by fluidization.

d) Another use for semicoke—this time outside the field of coke oven operations—is the sintering of iron ore, for which purpose the iron and steel industry uses coke dust. This dust is becoming increasingly difficult to obtain; semicoke can probably be used to replace it. Investigations of the optimum quality and conditions of use have still to be carried out, but the possibility must not be neglected in the future.

It would therefore seem probable that, in the years to come, semicokes will find a wide market; for this reason, it is well worth while to study their manufacture.

The only process which has the advantage of having had a long period of industrial use is, once again, that using the rotary furnace. It has certain disadvantages: low capacity, difficulty of scaling-up, high operating and maintenance costs and a restricted temperature. For these reasons we considered it worth while to study another method, namely, fluidization.

It may be helpful to state that—in the first place—our object was the replacement of coke dust in " tamped " coke ovens. We therefore envisaged operation at relatively high temperatures (800°C). The coal which is available does not cake and, consequently, preoxidation in unnecessary. Finally, the industrial installation to be investigated would have to have a capacity of 10 tons/hour of semi-coke.*

Our trials were first of all carried out on the scale of 100 kg/hour (200 lb./hr) in the Cerchar laboratories at Verneuil and, subsequently, on a scale of 1 ton/hour at the Marienau Experimental Station, which consists of a pilot plant, jointly owned by the Charbonnages de France and the Iron & Steel Industry.

II. SURVEY OF VARIOUS POSSIBLE INDUSTRIAL SOLUTIONS

There are many ways of subjecting coal fines to the heat necessary to produce semicarbonization. We have already said that the method which is at present most widely used is that employing a rotary furnace which is externally heated. Internal

---

* These conditions only apply to the first investigations. The conditions might very well be different for problems which would arise subsequently.

heating can scarcely be used except in the case of fluidized beds or loose beds because —in those cases which concern us—we have to treat coal fines and not small particles.

This heating can be provided by means of partial combustion—with air or oxygen —or by the passage of hot gases, inert flue gases or recycled production gas. Another solution would be to create a fluidized bed by means of steam, which is more or less preheated; the additional heat necessary would be provided by heating the reactor externally.

Finally, we must for completeness' sake refer to a type of internal heating which does not necessarily involve fluidization; this is the method in which the heating is carried out by contact with a heated solid body—coke, semicoke or refractory " cakes ".

We shall now briefly survey the advantages and disadvantages of the different methods, in order to justify our choice.

1. *Rotary Furnace*

We made use of this technique, which has been known in France for at least 25 years. The furnace consists essentially of two metal tubes, set one above the other, through which the coal passes. The flue gases produced by a line of burners heat the lower tube externally and then heat the upper tube internally. The coal is, consequently, preheated to 300°C in the latter, by contact with the hot gases, and is then carbonized in the lower tube.

This system is marked by the following features:

The temperature rise is relatively slow. In fact 15 to 20 minutes of heating are needed to bring the coal to between 300°C and 550°C.

A clean gas is yielded, that is, a gas which is not diluted by the presence of noncombustible gases; this is in contrast to what occurs in most processes which employ internal heating. This gas has a calorific value (dry basis) of the order of 7000 kcal/m³ (700 B.t.u./cu. ft.).

It is impossible to raise the temperature of the semicoke above 550°C (which corresponds to a volatile matter index of an average of 15%) without running the risk of causing buckling of the lower tube. The use of special steels would enable this limit to be raised quite considerably, but the cost would be prohibitive.

We ought to add that the installations which we know are capable of producing from one to two tons/hour of semicoke, whereas we wish to construct a plant with a capacity 10 times as great. The " scaling up " of rotary furnaces faces us with very complicated thermal and mechanical problems.

2. *Internal Heating by Means of Air*

The heat is provided by partial combustion of the coal in the air used to bring about fluidization. The advantages of the system are as follows:

The installation is very simple and the operation of the furnace is an easy matter.

The temperature of carbonization can be very readily controlled by modifying the air-coal ratio. We know that this point is very important, because—in the particular case of antifissurant additives for coke ovens using the tamping technique—

the semicoke obtained at a temperature of 800°C is very much better than that obtained at 500°C.

On the other hand:

The gas is mixed with atmospheric nitrogen, so that its calorific value (dry basis) is of the order of 1300 kcal/m³ (130 B.t.u./cu. ft.).

It might be feared that the tar would become oxidized and, consequently, lose its value. This is, it is true, only a hypothesis, since no investigation has settled this question as yet.

The gas carries along with it very fine dusts which considerably hamper condensation and decantation of the tars. This difficulty is also inherent in the fluidization processes.

3. Internal Heating by Means of Oxygen

The advantage of this process over the method previously described is that the quality of the gas is preserved, since it is no longer diluted by the atmospheric nitrogen. The disadvantage lies in the cost of the oxygen, which is virtually prohibitive, and also of the steam which is injected with the oxygen.

4. Internal Heating by Means of Inert Flue Gases

In this instance the heat is provided by the sensible heat from the flue gases obtained by burning any combustible gas in a pressurized combustion chamber. This eliminates with certainty any oxidation of the tar and, of course, prevents combustion of the proportion of coal, necessary to provide the heat of reaction (approx. 5%). Since no tests have yet been made to study any possible oxidation of the tar, it is by no means certain that the first-named advantage does, in fact, play any part. The second remains unaffected.

Unfortunately, the gas cannot be utilized, since its calorific value is less than 500 kcal/m³ (50 B.t.u./cu. ft.). In addition the sensible heat carried by 1 cubic metre of flue gases is very much lower than the heat liberated by the amount of fuel which can be burnt in 1 cubic metre of air; this necessitates the supply of considerable quantities of gas and, consequently, calls for large and expensive installations.

5. Internal Heating by Means of Recycled Gas

The interest of this process lies in the fact that it enables us to conserve the quality of the gas produced and incidentally to avoid partial combustion of the semicoke.

There is, unfortunately, a major technological difficulty. It is necessary to supply to the recycled production gas the heat which it will transfer to the fluidized bed. This gas must be brought to a high temperature—say 1400°C—and this involves the use of regenerators. These devices necessitate complete dedusting of the gas, and it is hardly possible to carry out total dedusting without cooling the gas. This would give rise to thermal losses far too high for the process to be worthy of consideration.

6. External Heating

This brings us to envisage heating the fluidized bed externally; in this case the gas would contain few inert constituents. The actual fluidization can be achieved by the use of steam or of gas; either medium may—if necessary—be preheated.

The disadvantage of external heating lies in the difficulty of constructing large plants. In fluidized-bed installations, the throughput increases as the square of the diameter, while the surface area available for heat transfer only increases linearly. This means that it is only possible to consider the use of external heating for small units. It is possible to get round this difficulty by installing internal heating tubes; however, this may disturb the fluidization process and may also cause constructional difficulties.

To sum up, this process is ill suited for application in large industrial units.*

7. *Internal Heating by Means of Heated Solid Bodies*

The principle involved depends on supplying the heat by means of a heated solid body—called a heat carrier—which is brought into contact with the coal to be carbonized. This can be done in various ways, e.g.:

a) Using heat carriers consisting of refractory " cakes " which are heated in a stove. They are separated by screening from the semicoke obtained.

b) Using heat carriers consisting of semicoke heated in a separate apparatus, either by means of gas or by partial combustion. The heated semicoke is then mixed with cold semicoke; there are no disadvantages to this procedure, since the products involved are the same.

c) Using heat carriers consisting of pieces of coke heated by partial combustion. It is possible to use the coke which has just been discharged from a battery of coke ovens; this makes available a supply of heat which is virtually gratis. Unfortunately, the investment costs to be expected are high.

These processes have been studied in the laboratories at Verneuil. They offer undoubted possibilities, but—so far as we are aware—none of them has yet been introduced on an industrial scale. We should also add that they do not necessarily involve the employment of fluidization (which would need to be obtained by means of steam or of recycled gas), since it is possible to carry out the mixing by other means.

8. *Choice of Process*

Objections can be raised against several of the processes we have enumerated, of such a nature that they virtually preclude their industrial use. The factors in question are: the excessive cost of oxygen in the case of internal heating with oxygen; the fact that an unusable gas is produced in the case of internal heating by means of inert flue gases and that the apparatus in this instance would be too large; the very large constructional difficulties involved in making a plant for internal heating by means of recycled gas; and the restricted scale of installations employing external heating.

The process making use of external heating by means of heat carriers—with all the possible variants—is worth considering, but it has not yet been industrially developed.

This leaves us with two alternatives: either the rotary furnace or internal heating

---

* Nevertheless, the process is used in the plant at Rockdale. External heating seems to be principally used in this case to reduce the volume of gas produced and, in consequence, to economize on the condensation apparatus. In addition, it is only necessary to supply part of the heat, the remainder being furnished by partial combustion of the coal in the air blown through.

in a reactor with an air draught. The first process yields a semicoke which is some-times of inadequate quality; furthermore, the process is unsuitable for " scaling up ". The second method allows of the preparation of semicoke of very varied properties and—at least in certain cases—of better quality. The latter reason would almost be sufficient by itself to justify the adoption of this process. The principle disadvantage is the relatively poor quality of the gas produced; this is, however, not a very serious difficulty, since the gas can be used for many purposes in the plant, and, in addition, is not a very important item in the thermal " balance sheet ".

However this may be, these are the reasons which caused us to decide upon using fluidization by means of air. We also carried out trials, as described below, with oxygen and hot flue gases.

III. THE 100kg/hour (200lb/hr) FURNACE

These investigations were begun in 1949 at the Cerchar Laboratories at Verneuil, using a unit with a capacity of 100 kg/hr*. The design of this installation is shown in Fig. 1.

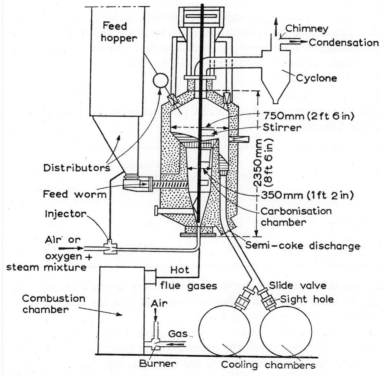

FIG. 1—Fluidized carbonization. 100 kg/hr plant.

---

* There were, in point of fact, several furnaces of the same capacity; we shall describe only the most recent of these.

F

1. *Description of the Apparatus*

The furnace proper is made up of two parts:

a) The carbonization chamber proper consists of a cone surmounted by a truncated cone. This is, in principle, the part of the plant in which the fluidization occurs. A grid can be set between the cone and the truncated cone; in this case the carbonization chamber is constituted by the truncated cone alone.

b) The storage bunker, which is situated above the carbonization chamber. As this is considerably larger than the carbonization chamber, there is sufficient room for an annular space which allows the semicoke to overflow.

The draught—consisting of air, a mixture of oxygen and steam or of hot flue gases—is blown into the lower part of the carbonization chamber, that is to say, at the summit of the cone.

The fuel is fed in in different ways:

  i) by a feed worm;

  ii) by dropping it from the top of the apparatus;
     air-tightness was assured, in this case, by the use of a rotary distributor.

  iii) by an injector through which the draught was blown.

The semicoke is discharged from the carbonization chamber by overflowing, after which it passes into the cooling vessels. The gas is dedusted in a cyclone and is then passed through a condenser. A rotary stirrer is placed inside the furnace; its use has been found advisable with certain caking coals.

2. *The Survey of the Tests*

Numerous tests were carried out in this furnace. In most of the tests we used one or other of the following coals.*

	Ash dry basis	Volatile matter on dry basis	Swelling index (AFNOR)
La Houve	10%	35%	0–1
Bruay	10%	31%	7½

It is interesting to note that the Bruay coal is very strongly caking. Nevertheless, we were able to treat it without difficulty, provided that the fluidization movements were activated by means of a rotary stirrer.

The draught was provided either by air, by oxygen (mixed with steam) or by hot flue gases. In the first two cases, the necessary heat was provided by combustion of part of the coal; this was about 5% of the total quantity for a bed temperature of 500°C.

Operational data—chosen from amongst the most typical cases—are shown in Table 1. All the runs were made at temperatures of the same order, i.e. between

* We also used intermediate qualities.

500°C and 600°C. The yields of semicoke are very similar. The principal difference is in the quality of gas obtained. The gas obtained by means of the air draught is poor—900 kcal/m³ (90 B.t.u./cu. ft.)—but can, nevertheless be put to industrial use. In addition we shall see further on that the gas obtained in the 1 ton/hour plant is better.* Working with an oxygen draught gives, as might be expected, a gas with a higher calorific value since it contains no nitrogen. The use of hot flue gases yields a very poor gas, so lean as to be virtually unusable.

TABLE 1

Tests carried out in the 100 kg/hr furnace

No. of test	84	139	201	233	236	190–197	241
Fluid medium used	Oxygen & steam mixture		←——— Air ———→			Hot flue gases	
Air m³/hr	—	—	47·5	37·5	40	—	—
Gas m³/hr	—	—	—	—	—	—	—
Flue gases m³/hr	—	—	—	—	—	72·5	72·5
Oxygen m³/hr	6·5	10	—	—	—	—	—
Steam m³/hr	27·8	47·5	—	—	—	—	—
Temperature °C	295	296	300	240	210	1000	1000
Coal treated	La Houve	Bruay	La Houve	Bruay	Bruay	Bruay	Bruay
Throughput (wet) coal in kg/hr	93	121	93	99·5	107	71·5	60·5
Temperature °C	195	105	65	95	15	70	15
Temperature of the bed °C	600	525	545	560	555	550	550
Material Balance Basis: 100 kg of dry coal							
Input Coal	100	100	100	100	100	—	—
Air	—	—	70	49·5	49·1	—	—
Lean gas							
Oxygen	10	11·8	—	—	—	—	—
Steam	30	39·3	—	—	—	—	—
Output Semi-coke	71	71·6	75·5	69·4	71·1	70·3	72·9
Gas in m³	17·5	13	56·5	43·2	42·8	116	135
Gas in kg	19·5	17	72·5	53·3	52·8	155	183·2
Calorific value (dry basis) of gas in kcal/m³	3545	4150	877	—	976	476	230

Conversion Factors (approximate):   B.t.u./s.c.f. $= \dfrac{\text{kcal/m}^3}{9\cdot55}$

ft³ $= \text{m}^3 \times 35\cdot3$
lb $= \text{kg} \times 2\cdot2$

* Even in the 100 kg/hr plant we frequently obtained gas of from 1200 to 1300 kcal/m³ (120 to 130 B.t.u./cu. ft.).

IV. THE 1 ton/hr INSTALLATION

This unit, which was built at Marienau Experimental Station, was put into operation for the first time in 1954. Since that time it has been used principally for the study of the technology of the process.

1. *Description of the Plant*

Fig. 2 is a diagrammatic representation of the layout and Fig. 3 is a photograph of the plant.

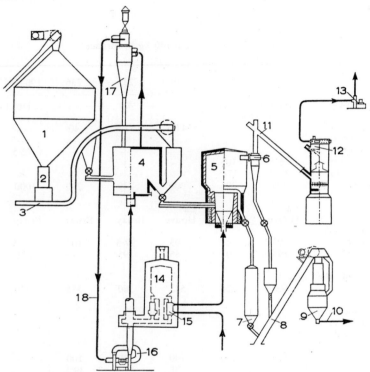

FIG. 2—Diagrammatic layout of the 1 ton/hr fluidization plant

1. Coal bunker	10. Discharge of semicoke via a Redler
2. Coal feeder	11. Raw-gas pipeline
3. Feed Redler	12. Tar washer
4. Preheating furnace	13. Gas extractor
5. Distillation furnace	14. Combustion chamber
6. Cyclones	15. Air reheater
7. Semicoke cooler	16. Fan for recycling flue gases
8. Bucket elevator	17. Cyclone in the recycling circuit
9. Semicoke feeder	18. Pipelines for recycled gas.

The installation appears to be complicated; the reason for this is that we wish to provide facilities for various experimental arrangements; however, in point of fact, the apparatus is essentially simple in design.

The principal element is the furnace proper (5). This has very largely the same shape as had the furnace in the small 100 kg/hr plant. The coal is fed in by means

FIG. 3—1 ton/hour fluidization plant.

of a worm-screw, approximately half-way up the fluidized charge. The semicoke " overflows " at the top into a cooling unit (7). The gases are discharged from the upper part of the chamber; they are hot dedusted in a cyclone and then cooled in a washer (12) where they are sprayed with recycled tar. This two-stage washer makes it possible to separate directly the hard pitch and part of the oil. The lightest oils and the water are condensed in a tubular apparatus which is not shown on the diagram.

In addition, we made provision for preheating of the coal, if this is desired. This operation can be executed—with the coal in a fluidized state—in the preheating furnace (4) which is supplied with hot flue gases from the furnace (14). We would recall that the object of this procedure is to reduce combustion of the coal during the carbonization proper, thus making it possible to improve the gas and to raise the throughput capacity of the fluid carbonizer. The preheating unit may also be used for oxidation of the coal. Finally, the draught air may be preheated by means of a metal exchanger inserted in the furnace (14).

The second fluidization furnace, similar to that marked at (5) on the drawing but of different size, may be used to study carbonization carried out with a mixture of oxygen and steam. Since this system is not of such topical interest as the air fluidization method, it has not been used.

2. Survey of the Trials

Hitherto, our tests have been directed towards the study of the technological problems involved in producing an industrial plant, rather than towards setting up balance sheets. In a word, we have sought, in the first place, to achieve regular and reliable operation, envisaging the preparation of material and thermal " balance sheets ", once the installation was functioning quite satisfactorily.

The principal difficulties we encountered were as follows:

a) *Assuring a smooth supply of coal.* This problem is complicated by the fact that it is necessary to attain simultaneously (a) a regular flow—the throughput being controllable at any moment—and (b) a gas seal between the coal hopper, which is at atmospheric pressure, and the furnace, which is at a higher pressure. This occasions a risk of blowbacks of gas and tar, the latter condensing in the distribution elements and causing blockages. In practice, when dry coal is used it is sufficient to design the hoppers and distributors suitably for the problem to be eliminated; this is, however, not true if it is desired to avoid the necessity of carrying out previous drying, as is desirable for the sake of the economical operation of the process.

The problem is somewhat simpler if the moist coal be fed into a fluidized-bed " dryer-preheater ", instead of into the furnace itself. In this case, any blowbacks which might occur can do no more than carry steam along; the condensation of this steam on the coal—which is already moist—is much less troublesome than that of the tar. Since we shall very probably make use of preheating in our proposed industrial installation, we expect to be able to solve this problem of feeding the plant without great difficulty.

b) *To avoid the formation of clinker in the bed.* In the first trials, we were using a grid, on which we observed—after some 12 hours of operation—the formation of clinker. No clinker whatsoever was produced once we had removed the grid; this meant that the furnace terminated—at its lower end—in a cone, through the point of which the draught air was supplied. The explanation is simple: the air issuing from the inlet and striking the grid does so at a speed too low to enable it to fluidize the coarse particles; these burn in situ, thus reaching the ash fusion temperature. If the lower part of the furnace is formed by a cone, the coarsest particles cannot fall below the level where the speed of the air is sufficient to fluidize them. Since these coarsest particles are no longer left at the bottom of the bed, they are situated sufficiently far up in the main portion of the fluidized mass for there to be no risk of their reaching the ash-fusion temperature.

c) *To ensure proper recovery of the products·present in the gas.* The gas carries along with it the finest particles of semicoke, and also, of course, the condensable products (water and tar, the latter in the form of vapour). Sudden cooling would be dangerous, since it would cause simultaneous deposition of the water, the oil, and the dust. Decantation would be very difficult in this case. For this reason we adopted a solution which enabled us:

  i) To stop the solid particles by means of a hot deduster. At present it appears that an adequate degree of dedusting can be obtained by the use of suitably designed cyclones.
  ii) To condense the pitch during the first cooling to a carefully controlled temperature (220°C to 240°C, according to the operating conditions). This pitch contains almost the entire quantity of dust which had passed through the cyclones.
  iii) Following this, to cause condensation of the heaviest oils by spraying with recycled oil.
  iv) Finally, to bring down the light oils and the water. Since these liquids contain virtually no dust, they are easy to separate.

d) *To cool the semi-coke.* It would seem that the best method of doing this consists of fluidizing by means of cold flue gases, coupled with water injection.

All the devices mentioned above are, at the moment of writing, either fully developed or undergoing trial.

We are at present engaged upon preparing balance sheets, but our results are not yet sufficiently conclusive to allow us to publish them.

V. QUALITY OF THE PRODUCTS OBTAINED

1. *Semicoke*

Even when we used high-volatile, weakly caking coals,* we observed that the semicoke was a fused product and was relatively friable. In particular, we were able to compare the semicoke produced in a rotary furnace with that produced in a fluidized bed at very similar temperatures (500°C), using the same coal (dry long-flame coal). The two products are very different. In the first case, the coal particles have maintained their shape and structure; only their colour has changed slightly

---

* Volatile matter content on the dry basis 35%; crucible swelling index (AFNOR) = 1.

and they are now brown, instead of black.   As opposed to this, the semicoke obtained by fluidization is made up of swollen particles, which have obviously been subject to a degree of fusion.   On the other hand, the semicoke prepared at temperatures so widely different as 500°C and 800°C cannot be distinguished by the naked eye. The difference in appearance and structure between the semicoke from the rotary furnace and that from the fluidized bed does not, therefore, depend on the temperature reached, but on the rate of heating; in the first instance the final temperature is reached in about 30 minutes, as against less than 1 minute in the second case.

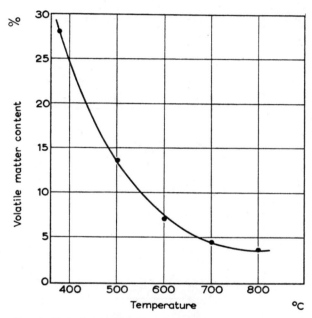

FIG. 4—Volatile matter index of semicoke as a function of the temperature of the furnace

The semicoke produced by fluidization is of very uniform quality for clearly-defined conditions of operation. The volatile matter content is determined very accurately indeed by the furnace temperature; the accuracy is of the order of $\pm 0.5\%$. Fig. 4 shows the correlation which we were able to obtain experimentally.

2. *Gas*

The gas obtained by fluidization with air necessarily contains an appreciable quantity of nitrogen. Its composition depends on the temperature at which it is fed into the furnace. We have given in Fig. 5 a diagram showing the composition of the gas as a function of the temperature. This diagram must be considered as provisional, since certain parameters have not yet been investigated. In particular, it would seem that the bed height has an influence which we have not yet been able to clarify.

In addition, we must point out that this diagram corresponds to operations during which the coal is fed in while it is both cold and dry (3% to 4% of moisture).

It is perfectly clear that, the more heat it is necessary to supply per ton of dry coal, the higher will be the nitrogen and CO_2 contents of the gas. For example, we can see from the diagram that, during operation at 700°C, the gas contains 65% of nitrogen and 11·5% of CO_2. At the same temperature, but using a feed coal with 13·5% of moisture, we obtained a gas having 71% of nitrogen and 12·5% of CO_2.

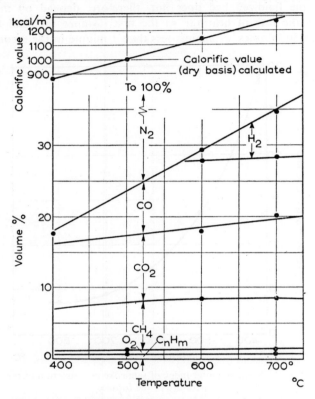

FIG. 5—Composition of the gas as a function of temperature

Conversely, a test run carried out with coal preheated to 220°C and air at a temperature of 445°C gave a gas with 54% of nitrogen and 10% of CO_2. The calculated calorific values for these three different gases were 1250, 900 and 2200 kcal/m³ (125, 90, and 220 B.t.u./cu. ft.) respectively.

3. Tars

We have made very little progress with this question as yet, since we have been principally occupied with problems of a technological character; that is to say, with producing a simple type of condenser allowing of industrial operation. The study of the tars is to be undertaken in the near future.

VI. STUDY OF AN INDUSTRIAL UNIT

For reasons which we set out in Section II (and which are very largely based on the trials described in the succeeding sections) we decided to investigate an industrial unit having a capacity of 10 ton/hr (20,000 lb/hr) and operating by means of internal heating with an air draught. Once we had decided upon the process to be used, other points still remained to be settled. It would be possible, for instance, to carry out previous pre-heating of the coal up to about 300°C. that is to say, up to its decompostion limit, by the use of air at a temperature up to 500°C. Calculation shows that this would provide—outside the carbonization apparatus—approximately half the heat necessary to carbonize the coal at 800°C. In consequence of this, it would be possible to carbonize twice as much coal with the same flow of air; this would improve the quality of the gas and would permit the use of smaller plant. Since it is necessary to " scale up " by a factor of 10, to go from our present plant to the type we envisage as being the normal industrial unit, the semicarbonization furnace can be scaled up by a factor of 5; this is obviously much simpler.

Another aspect of the question which is of a purely technological nature is the following: we have hitherto worked with coal dried to about 3% or 4% of moisture. Drying was implicitly considered as a necessary preliminary operation. There are two possibilities of eliminating this preheating:

a) *By feeding the air furnace directly with moist coal*—On one occasion the trial was run for about 12 hours. Apart from a few practical difficulties, which do not seem to be insoluble, the installation operated quite smoothly. This solution gives rise to a very simple installation, since it consists of only one element. On the other hand, the gas is of fairly poor quality, but is still usable (900 kcal/m³). Finally, the apparatus must be relatively large, since the quantity of draught air needed per ton of coal is higher than is the case with dry coal. This solution may therefore be envisaged as worthy of consideration, but it is probable that the following suggestion will be more satisfactory.

b) *By carrying out the drying at the same time as the preheating*—The supply is less difficult to provide than in the preceding case, because there is no risk of obstruction being caused by the condensation of tar. It is very probable that the two operations can be carried out simultaneously and we intend to try to confirm this in practice. Our present investigations of the industrial unit will be directed towards this end.

Finally, the transition from the 1 ton per hour plant to a unit yielding 10 tons per hour of semicoke presents problems of " scaling up " which must not be underestimated. In particular, we are seeking to avoid an excessive increase in the height of the coal bed, as this would involve both excessively large apparatus and a very high draught pressure. This question is at present being investigated.

We have attempted in the present paper to describe our work up to the point we have reached at present.

We should point out that, at the moment of writing (February 1956), the 1 ton/hr plant which was used to perform our last trials is to be modified so as to allow of operation over long periods; this is not possible with the apparatus which we have available at the moment. The conclusions we have formulated must be considered as provisional until we have been able to carry out genuine industrial operations. In point of fact, while it is improbable that the main ideas will be appreciably altered, it is, of course, possible that certain details will no longer hold good a few months hence.

DISCUSSION

Mr. J. Owen (*National Coal Board, Stoke Orchard*):

First of all, I would like to pay a tribute to the admirable paper we have just heard by Messrs. Peytavy and Foch. Having been involved in similar work myself, I appreciate the many penetrating points they have made. In particular, their description of difficulties carries conviction.

I would now like to say a little about our recent work on fluid carbonization here. Firstly, we have made some measurements on the total heat required for carbonizing low-rank coals, similar in type to those Messrs. Peytavy and Foch have been using. The measurement of heat requirements on small-scale units is usually an exacting task, and if the results are to be useful it demands considerable experimental skill. The main difficulty lies in the fact that heat losses in a small plant are very much larger than the heat being measured, and hence large errors are difficult to avoid. Here we used a difference method for determining the total quantity of heat which is required to carbonize coal.

Fig. A.

Briefly, our plant is started up and then brought to temperature by adjustment of the coal feed rate. Care is taken in setting compensating heaters which are fitted to the vessel, so there is no heat flowing either into or out of the reactor. With a constant fluidizing-gas rate, there is only one coal feed rate with which this can be done. In spite of all care, of course, some heat is inevitably lost. However, the plant is allowed to settle to steady conditions while the appropriate measurements are made. This constitutes the first part of our run only, i.e. the blank determination. Then electrical heaters, which are set in the fluid bed, are switched on and the coal feed rate has to be increased until steady conditions are reached again. The same bed temperature is maintained as in the first part of the run. The heat requirement is then deduced from the electrical heat, which we can measure quite accurately, and from the increase in the coal feed rate. The small heat losses which occur during the first part of the determination also occur in the second and therefore do not enter into our estimates.

The results we have obtained are shown in Fig. A. These are experimental results obtained on non-caking (Binley) coal with a volatile matter content of about 40%. The total coking heat in B.t.u./lb. of dry coal is plotted against carbonizing temperature.

For comparison purposes, a line has been drawn which represents the sensible heat requirement assuming a constant specific heat for the coal. The sensible heat line has no physical significance since both the coal composition and specific heat are changing with temperature. It is included to show that the total heat which must be added to carbonize this particular coal is in excess, and above 600°C greatly in excess, of the sensible heat requirement. The unwelcome significance of this graph is that it makes the plant larger by a factor of two or three.

The second point I would like to talk about is the loss of volatile matter that is inevitable when a recycle process is used. A recycle process, for those who are not familiar with it, is one in which some of the coke in the reactor is withdrawn and circulated into a second vessel. In the second vessel this coke is blown with air and reaches a temperature greatly in excess of the carbonizing temperature. The reheated coke, after combustion, is then returned to the reactor; the sensible heat which it carried being used to heat up the incoming fresh coal. Fig. B shows two experimental loss in weight versus time curves which we obtained in the laboratory at temperatures of 475°C and 500°C. We use these curves to deduce what will happen in the recycle carbonizing plant. First of all, we arbitrarily made the combustor and reactor sizes equal; then at any time, half of the solid in the system must be in the reactor and half in the combustor. We also fixed the combustor temperature at 500°C and the

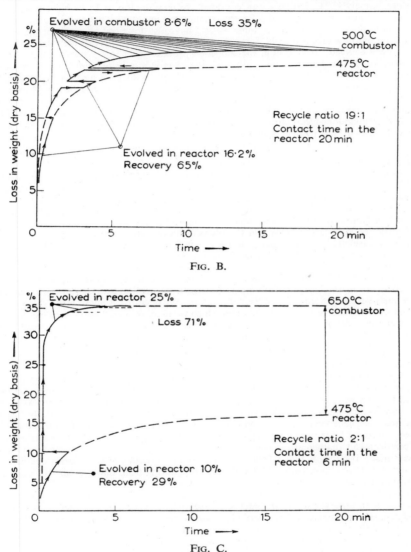

Fig. B.

Fig. C.

reactor temperature at 475°C. It follows from the heat balance that we must recycle 19 parts of coke for every 1 part of feed coal. Thus, if the total contact time is 20 minutes, incoming coal into the reactor spent, on an average, alternate minutes in the reactor and the combustor. This is shown in the diagram by alternating lines. Coal coming into the reactor decomposes along the lower of the two curves; it then goes up to the combustor and that part of the journey is represented by an arrow going to the left. In the combustor it spends another minute and decomposes this time along the line which corresponds to the 500° decomposition line. It returns to the reactor and decomposes a little more at 475°C, and so on. The alternating steps can be summed to give the relative amounts of volatile matter evolved. In the reactor this is 16·2% and in the combustor, 8%. That is, roughly one third of the total volatile matter is lost and leaves the combustor in the waste flue gases. At first sight, it would appear that we could save some of this waste by reducing the recycle ratio by circulating less coke. But on getting down to it we find that it is not so. In Fig. C we are using the same reactor temperature, namely 475°C, but have now cut down the recycle ratio to 2 : 1. Now as we supply the same amount of heat in less recycled coke, the combustor temperature has to be increased to 650°C. Then by a procedure similar to the example which I have just described we find that the recovery of volatile matter has now dropped to 29% and that the loss amounts to 71% of the total volatile matter which has been evolved. In addition, the semicoke product from this process is lower in volatile content than for the previous example, although the reactor was being run at 475°C in each case. Summing up, we can say that the recycling of hot coke undoubtedly gives a gas of better quality from the reactor than a system which uses air as the fluidizing gas such as that described by Monsieur Foch. But the recycle system is very wasteful in improving the gas quality. Furthermore, for any given throughput and especially if a high recycle ratio is needed, then the plant will be very large. For these reasons we have abandoned the combustion method ourselves, but I must add that we may have to go back to it, if we ever have to treat a coal which cokes.

AUTHOR (MONSIEUR P. FOCH):

Mr. Owen has described an experimental method of determining the heat of carbonization which is really most ingenious, and must have given him a good deal of trouble to develop; it certainly is a good means of determining the heat of reaction. I confess, however, it is difficult to reply with any degree of certainty today whether our results agree with his or not; the reason would be that, whereas he worked in a laboratory with a laboratory-scale plant and laboratory equipment, we worked on a semi-industrial, or even larger, scale and the phenomena (which are equally difficult to assess and express in each case) are less easy to get at, as it were, in dealing with a larger plant. As I have already said, we set up thermal and material balance sheets, but the figures are provisional. In any case, I have not got the figures in mind; they are fairly difficult to remember. Nevertheless, I am a little surprised at the importance which the heat of carbonization seems to take on. It would have seemed to me that, as far as we can judge from operations with the semi-industrial plant, it is the case that there is a fairly substantial quantity of heat of reaction. We operated at about 600°C, also at 500°C or 800°C, and as far as can be seen from the plant which we used, it would be the sensible heat which is important and the heat of reaction less so. Nevertheless, it is difficult to be certain. It will be possible to discuss this in greater detail later, when we have more accurate figures available.

DR. J. BRONOWSKI (*National Coal Board, Stoke Orchard*):

That part of what Mr. Owen has just said which concerned the heat needed to carbonize coal in a fluid bed may seem at odds with what Monsieur Foch told us in his paper. Mr. Owen has said, and illustrated the fact with a diagram, that if you carbonize a high-volatile coal above 600°C, the heat required may be very much higher than you expect. Monsieur Foch said that the fluid-bed carbonizer which he and Monsieur Peytavy described seems to work equally well at 500°C and 800°C.

We were puzzled by the same discrepancy two years ago, and we therefore undertook a fundamental physical and mathematical study in the Physics Department here to find out how these differences arise. It happens that I have recently given an account of this work (together with the work which Mr. Owen described), and I will begin by quoting from that account the description of the method and apparatus we used:

" Some two years ago our laboratory, and chiefly Dr. Millard,[1] set out to analyse temperature distributions in an experimental oven which was essentially a section of a full-scale coke oven. Very large differences in temperature and thermal constants are present in such a system. For instance temperatures of 100°C and 800°C, and thermal conductivities of 4×10^{-4} cal/cm sec deg and 80×10^{-4} cal/cm sec deg may be found at the same time in different parts of the oven. We decided to study the fundamental physics of such a system, and to this end we attempted to solve the resulting equation of heat flow across the oven in mathematical form. This is not possible analytically; so an electrical analogue technique due to the late Dr. G. Liebmann[2] was used. This is an electrical calculating machine which produces a series of instantaneous solutions to the heat flow equation for successive instants in time, the solutions following one another like the frames in a cinematograph film. Voltage is made analogous to temperature, current to heat flux, and electrical conductance to thermal conductance. Heat capacity is not simulated by electrical capacity, since then the analogy would be complete, and time would run on uncontrollably in the analogue as it does in the oven. Instead, the effect of heat capacity is simulated by making the solution for each instant of time dependent to a chosen degree on that for the preceding instant. In this way time in the analogue can be started and stopped at will, and adjustments can be made in the course of the work."

When we used the machine, which I have described, to follow the known changes of temperature through a coke oven, we found that we had to make it simulate large absorptions of heat in the coal over one temperature range, and a large production of heat over another. I give a diagram (Fig. D) of our findings, and I quote again the comments which I have made on this elsewhere.

" In the diagram, estimates of the cumulative heats required to carbonize two coals obtained in this way are plotted against the temperature of carbonization. For comparison, the heat required by an inert material of specific heat 0·25 is also plotted. It will be seen that between about 450°C and 700°C the slopes of the graphs for coal are much larger than the slope for the inert material, and this shows that relatively large quantities of heat are absorbed by the coal. This heat is partly or wholly given back at higher temperatures. We interpret these results as evidence that there is an endothermic reaction of carbonization at temperatures below about 700°C, followed by an exothermic reaction

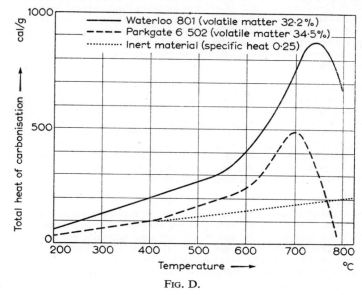

FIG. D.

later. One coal, Parkgate 6, (Coal Rank Code No. 502, V.M. 34·5%) is a coking coal. The other, Waterloo, (C.R.C. 801, V.M. 32·2%) is a low rank coal not normally carbonized. It can be seen that the heat required by the coking coal up to 750°C, is about twice, but by the low rank coal about five times, that required by the inert material. Such large heats of reaction were unexpected."

Thus Fig. D shows how it is that working a carbonization process at 800°C may be just as economic in heat as at 500°C. You will see that, with some coals, the exothermic reaction which begins at about 700°C has liberated enough heat, by the time that it reaches 800°C, to have got back almost all the heat that it absorbed at lower temperatures. Therefore it may well be that 500°C and 800°C are precisely the temperatures at which the conditions for carbonization in a fluid bed are most favourable. But we must not conclude that they will therefore be equally favourable between these temperatures. On the contrary, the diagram shows that they are likely to be most unfavourable, because they are likely to demand most heat, between 650°C and 750°C.

AUTHOR (MONSIEUR P. FOCH):

I am very interested by the suggestion which has just been made by Dr. Bronowski in explaining the slide and it seems a very good explanation; and in fact, it is true that we have most frequently worked either under 500°C or at 800°C. Occasionally we did run at 600°C, one or two runs being made, but figures were not taken for the thermal balance sheets. We made another run at 700°C. I would suggest that the peak may not lie at exactly the same place in that case. I think that the suggestion is a very fruitful one and a possible explanation of the reason why Mr. Owen and I do not appear to agree at the moment.

AUTHOR (MONSIEUR A. PEYTAVY):

In reply to the second question put by Mr. Owen, I would say that I was very interested by the information he gave regarding the operation of a carbonization plant with heating by means of recycling the hot coke.

We have not, for our part, used this process as yet, but it so happens that we are just about to study the possibilities of applying it at Verneuil; this information will, therefore, be most welcome.

It is particularly noticeable that the improvement of gas obtained in this way corresponds to a loss of volatile matter in a "combustor", which loss is the greater (if the apparatus has the correct dimensions) the lower the rate of recycling, i.e. the greater is the difference of temperature between the "reactor" and the "combustor".

In addition, Mr. Owen considers that an important advantage of the process is that it allows of carbonizing coking coals.

I would like to point out that at Verneuil we have treated (in the apparatus with a throughput of 100 kg/hr which we have described) coals of all types, including the Bruay coal (swelling index AFNOR: 7·5); we also treated other coals with swelling indexes up to 9. This treatment was carried out without adding nonfusing material in the carbonizer which contains for the most part the semicoke already formed; the only other features is a regular stirring of the bed by means of a low-powered mechanical stirrer. This device provides another solution to the problem; it is not yet absolutely proven that the stirrer is indispensable.

DR. R. J. MORLEY (*National Coal Board, London*):

I have four questions to ask the authors: Could they please tell us whether there is any reaction between the steam and the semicoke at the highest temperatures used? This is an unwanted reaction, and if it occurred, it would be an additional reason for drying the coal. I would have thought that perhaps with the very reactive semicoke, it would have occurred at 800°C. The second question is, what was the depth of the bed and the residence time in the fluidized bed? The third question is, how much dust, as a proportion of the coal fed, was caught in the cyclone? The fourth question is in connection with the external cyclone. Was there any trouble due to tar condensing in the leg coming down from the cyclone—the solids discharge line from the cyclone?

AUTHOR (MONSIEUR P. FOCH):

I shall reply to the questions of Dr. Morley in order. Is there any reaction between the steam and the coke? This must, of course, be the steam from the moisture in the coal as we do not inject steam. It is a matter which would need to be determined with some accuracy, but it would seem doubtful that there is any appreciable reaction below 800°C. Question 2, the height of the bed is between 2 metres and 3 metres and the residence time (or contact time) is of the order of half an hour, perhaps slightly more, depending on the rate of throughput. Question 3 relates to the quantity of dust trapped as a percentage of the coal charged. This is fairly high, since work is carried out in turbulent conditions. There is a fairly considerable quantity of fine dust, about 10% to 15%. This is not very troublesome to deal with. With regard to the fourth question, whether there have been difficulties with the condensation of tar, the answer is no, not now. We have had trouble with this in the past. Various solutions were tried, including external heating of the cyclone. The method adopted today is simply to put heat insulation around the cyclone and that appears to be satisfactory.

IR. E. GRAND'RY (*Société Carbochimique Service des Recherches, Tertre*):

Have any special arrangements been made—double envelopes or anything of that kind—to ensure that the cyclone is maintained below dew point?

AUTHOR (MONSIEUR P. FOCH):

No, the gases are blown into the cyclone at a fairly high temperature, and it appears from present experience to be adequate to have the heat insulation round the cyclone.

MR. H. D. GREENWOOD (*National Coal Board, London*):

I was very interested to read the very useful survey by Monsieur Foch on the various possible methods of making char or low-temperature coke, and I entirely agree with his conclusions and the reason which certain types of processes have been rejected as unsuitable.

Mr. Owen has told us of some of the difficulties associated with fluidization methods and some of the alternative methods of operating this type of process.

I would like to emphasize the importance, as the authors did, of obtaining adequate revenue from the gas produced. I doubt whether the process can be economical unless you get some revenue from the gas made, and a low-grade gas cannot always be utilized economically. I would also like to emphasize that any process involving the circulation of very large quantities of gas will be expensive not only in capital but also in operating costs.

Mention is not made in the survey of the process developed by the Ruhrgas Co., in which powdered coal is carbonized in a bed of heated small coke. The primary object of this process is gas production, the hot coke and waste gases evolved in preheating both being fed direct to a boiler furnace. The process could, of course, be adapted to operate at lower temperatures to make a char. A plant to carbonize about 200 tons of coal per day is being erected.

There are three main ways in which we, in this country, can use low-temperature chars:—

(1) By briquetting to produce a domestic fuel—as was described to us yesterday.
(2) For blending, so as to improve the quality of blast-furnace or metallurgical coke as already mentioned.
(3) Blending with different coals to improve the reactivity of cokes.

So far as an improved grade of blast-furnace coke is concerned, our conditions are quite different from those in France; in Lorraine the practice has been to import quite large quantities of coking coal from the Ruhr. The potential saving by reducing the import of coal by blending with char, etc., is therefore considerable. In this country the increase in value of coke, obtained by increasing the strength, is relatively small.

Dr. G. I. Jenkins (*National Coal Board, Stoke Orchard*):

Messieurs Peytavy and Foch discussed four principal difficulties which they have encountered in the operation of their fluidized carbonizers. Of these difficulties the one which has probably caused most trouble at this Establishment is the recovery of the gaseous and vapour products. The troubles have arisen from the presence of the fine particles of the semicoke in the exit material. This point was the subject of some discussion this morning. For example, Dr. Morley was asking if there was trouble in the cyclone leg, caused by the condensation of tar. It would be very interesting to know if Messieurs Peytavy and Foch have considered using a system which prevents the semicoke leaving the reaction system. This can be done, at least in theory, by means of an internal cyclone and a simple fractionator, which is integral with the top flange of the carbonizing vessel. The arrangement is shown in

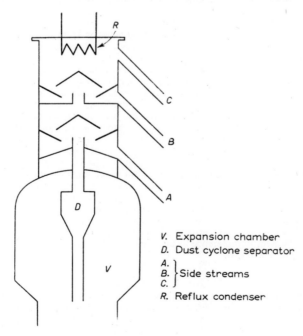

V. Expansion chamber
D. Dust cyclone separator
A.
B. } Side streams
C.
R. Reflux condenser

Fig. E.

Fig. E. The expansion chamber V reduces the linear velocity and minimizes the dust loading. The major portion of the fine semicoke is returned to the fluidized bed by the internal cyclone D but an appreciable amount is carried forward by the vapour stream. This passes into the fractionator, placed directly on top of the carbonizing vessel, where the semicoke is washed out and taken off as a slurry in the side-stream, A. The middle oil can be taken off at B and the light oil and gas through the overhead, C. This system has many advantages. There is no long transfer line from the vessel to the recovery system, so there is no danger of blockage. There is no condensation of tar in the leg of the cyclone, since the cyclone is essentially at reaction temperature. I would like to ask Messieurs Peytavy and Foch whether they have considered using this. It has been used in the oil industry, where, recently, it has been incorporated in the plants which produce semicoke by the cracking of very heavy residual oils.

AUTHOR (MONSIEUR A. PEYTAVY):

I thank Dr. Jenkins for the information which he has given us on the dedusting and condensation system which he described.

The system used at Marienau is similar, the main difference being that it is not placed on top of the oven, but in the immediate vicinity.

Our apparatus also is provided with a cyclone—which is fitted externally—and with a two-stage condensation column. In the first stage, the products leaving the cyclone are cooled to about 250°C; the pitch separates out, carrying with it the residual dust. Part of the oil separates in the second stage, the other part being condensed in the tubular condenser which is fitted at the exit from the column.

We have hitherto used an external cyclone, because it is much easier to check its operation; this was a great convenience in the first trials. At the moment, however, we are studying the installation of an internal cyclone; this would have the advantage of automatically recycling the fine particles whose carbonization is—in the present installation—generally less complete than those forming the remainder of the charge. Nevertheless, from the point of view of the dedusting operation, this arrangement will not make the problem any easier, since it occasions an over-loading of the cyclone.

DR. N. THORP (National Coal Board, Stoke Orchard):

I would like to ask a question connected with the scale-up mentioned by Messieurs Peytavy and Foch. By using published work on the kinetics of combustion of metallugical coke in a fluid bed, we were able to calculate the probable pattern of heat release in fluid bed carbonization, when air is used as the fluidizing gas. Preliminary experimental evidence suggests that semicoke oxidation exhibits a similar behaviour to that of metallurgical coke. The conclusion from this work may have a bearing on one of the aspects of scaling-up a fluid bed carbonizer. In general, the throughput of a fluidized bed is controlled not by the time required for carbonization, but by the heat release from oxidation of the semicoke. Some of our findings are given in graphical form in Fig. F.

The bed height in feet at which the exit oxygen partial pressure from a fluid bed using air as fluidizing gas is 0·01 atmos. (1% oxygen fluidizing gas) is plotted as the ordinate against the bed temperature in °C as abscissae. This is shown for two fluidizing velocities, 1 ft./sec and 0·65 ft./sec, considering the bed to be 1 sq. ft. cross-section and the coal density to be 20 lb./cu. ft. If we take a plant working at say 550°C, with a 5 ft. bed, then an increase in the fluidizing velocity will allow of an increase in throughput, i.e. an increase from the 0·65 ft./sec line to the 1·0 ft./sec line. At 1 ft./sec more heat will be generated and an increase in throughput will result. This cannot be carried on to excess, because the fluidizing velocity is limited to avoid excessive carry-over from the bed; consequently this figure of 1 ft./sec is tending towards the limit which might be used. If the bed is at 550°C, then an increase in fluidizing velocity above 1 ft./sec will lead to incomplete combustion if we have a bed about 5 ft. high; the oxygen in the exit gas is in excess of 0·01 atm. At much lower temperatures the situation is similar, but a much greater bed height is required to complete the oxidation step. These calculations, while based on a cross-section area of 1 sq. ft. in the figure, are unaffected by this parameter. Hence in scaling-up from perhaps a 1 ton per hour to a 10 ton per hour plant, an increase in bed diameter is indicated, in preference to an increase in bed height, so that excessive bed heights in scale-up may be readily avoided.

AUTHOR (MONSIEUR P. FOCH):

I believe that Dr. Thorp has clearly described the factors which determine the diameter of the reactor. As he said, they work at temperatures of about 800°C, and the temperature, and in fact the operation as a whole, is controlled by the air/coal ratio. That is to say, if it is desired to work with a given throughput of coal, the throughput of air is already fixed by that predetermined ratio. Consequently, it is necessary to choose the cross-section of the reactor so as to have an acceptable air

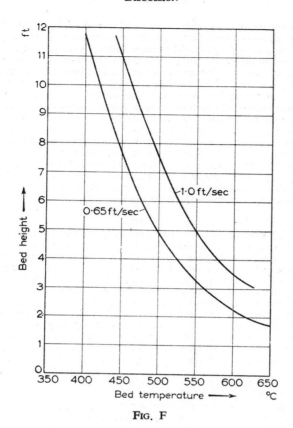

FIG. F

velocity; i.e. a velocity which does not entrain too much dust. The velocity is, in principle, limited by the degree of dust entrainment which it involves. The limiting factor is, surprising though it may seem, apparently the efficiency of dedusting at the exit from the plant. The second point Dr. Thorp mentioned is that it is not desirable—in fact there is no reason at all—to increase bed height. I am perfectly in agreement with this statement, in theory, but unfortunately in practice it is not quite so easy, since there is another difficulty. If you remember the plant which we described—in the drawing shown as Fig. A—the reactor part of the plant is essentially the conical part; as I indicated a little earlier this makes use of a bed height from 2½ to 3 metres. If it is desired to increase throughput of the plant by 10 times, this involves an increase in the cross-section by 10 times; one does not need to be an aerodynamic expert to see that the very flat, very open cone thus produced gives a ridiculous shape to the plant and the flow conditions are quite impractical. Consequently, while I agree with Dr. Thorp's statement as a matter of theory, unfortunately in practice it may be necessary to increase the bed height.

Mr. A. Szpilewicz (*Ministry of Iron and Steel, Poland*):

I wish to make some comments, not so much on the paper by Messrs. Foch and Peytavy, but rather to give some general indications on research being done at present in Poland. We too are interested in the fluidized carbonization process, but we have made trials to bring this about in a very short residence time, some seconds only; these tests have been done on very high-volatile coals, Upper Silesian coals with a volatile content of 30% to 40%. This coal is ground to the sizes which are normal for carbonization, i.e. between 95% and 100% minus 3 millimetres. The coal is then heated so as to make it plastic in the first chamber. It goes into a second chamber, still in the plastic state, where it remains for some seconds for a preliminary degasification. This homogeneous, viscous paste then goes into a press where briquettes are made continuously, under pressure of from 1·5 atm.

G

to 4 atm. The briquettes are mostly cylindrical in form, 60 mm in diameter and 60 mm high. The paste is pressed out of the press automatically, and the pressure also automatically regulated, according to the content of gas still in the paste. The temperature, of course, must be regulated in such a way that it is always within the plastic range of the coke. The briquettes then undergo a secondary degasification in the final chamber; they are heated in this chamber at 850°C and then come out of the chamber with a volatile content of about 5% and a drum index of 5 to 6 (i.e. 5/6 over 10 mm: Micum test). The idea on which this new process is based has been proposed and developed by a Russian author—Sapozhnikov—who published a report on this subject last year and his idea gave us the suggestion for the trials we carried out at the Coal Research Institute at Zabrze in Upper Silesia. This process is of very great interest in our country because, as you know, good coking coal is rare in Upper Silesia. This process could open up new methods of treatment and very much improve the general economic position of coal, particularly for the production of metallurgical coke, which we need very badly. I would emphasize that what I have told you is still in the laboratory and research stage. We know that we have a long way to go. Technical problems must still be solved, and there are problems as to what we should do to upgrade, or draw revenue from, byproducts and the gases coming from both stages; these problems have not yet been solved.

Mr. J. Owen (*National Coal Board, Stoke Orchard*):

We have been studying the properties of chars produced by the fluidization of a coal similar in properties to La Houve coal, discussed in the paper. The coal we used was virtually noncaking with a volatile matter of 39% dry basis. Making allowance for the difference in volatile matter of the two original coals, our results relating the volatile matter of the semicoke and the temperature of fluidization, fall very closely indeed to the curve presented, Fig. 4. Semicoke prepared at the extreme temperatures (375°C and 650°C) showed visual differences and these differences are accentuated in microscopic examination. The authors report differences in structure between semicoke prepared by rotary and by fluid bed methods. Our microscopic technique shows structural differences between semicoke of the same volatile content but produced by relatively minor changes in the fluidization process itself. The observations made in the paper refer to La Houve coal which has feebly coking properties. Can the authors give any information on the differences in semicoke quality obtained when the highly swelling Bruay coal was treated by the two processes—rotary carbonization and fluidization.

Author (Monsieur A. Peytavy):

We have no information regarding the plasticity of semicoke, since plasticity only applies to products which have a volatile matter content greater than that corresponding to the point of resolidification of the coal; this latter feature depends, in turn, on the temperature and the length of the heating period. This volatile matter content is of the order of 15%.

With lower volatile contents, the semicokes do not melt. It is, in fact, solely the products in this category which interest us in our problems of preparing additives for coke blends.

This is the reason why we have not studied the properties of fused semicokes.

Mr. J. Owen (*National Coal Board, Stoke Orchard*):

The authors note that when a feebly caking coal is treated in a fluid bed carbonizer the product shows evidence of fusion. Our work on semicoke produced from a coal of similar properties confirms this statement and this is illustrated in the photomicrographs included in Mr. Gregory's paper. The conclusion is reached in the paper that rate of heating as well as final temperature are the important criteria in deciding the structure of the semicoke. We have carried out plasticity experiments in the Gieseler apparatus and have shown that maximum fluidity is increased and softening temperature decreased by increasing the rate of heating the coal from 3°C/min to 10°C/min.

Have the authors any information on the plasticity of semicokes produced at low temperatures and if there is a progressive reduction in plasticity as the semicokes decrease in volatile content?

Author (Monsieur A. Peytavy):

First of all, I am very gratified to notice the agreement we have with Mr. Owen on the correlation between volatile matter and temperature of fluidization.

As far as the appearance of the semicoke is concerned, we have actually observed differences between products prepared at 375°C and at 650°C, but not between those prepared at 650°C and at 800°C. Nevertheless, these latter two products differ very markedly with regard to volatile matter, modulus of elasticity and density.

Regarding the Bruay coal, which we treated in a fluidized bed and which gives a well-fused semicoke, there is no shadow of doubt that in the rotary oven the product would be equally well fused;

however, in fact, precisely with the object of avoiding agglutination in the oven, this coal is not treated until it has been oxidized in air at about 350°C. In the case of coal which has been subjected to the same oxidation treatment in a fluidized bed at the same temperature as in the rotary oven, the fusion is still complete.

REFERENCES

1. MILLARD D. J. *Nature* **174**, 1099 (1954); *J. Inst. Fuel* **28**, 345 (1955).
2. LIEBMANN G. A new electrical analogue method for the solution of transient heat conduction problems *Trans. Amer. Soc. Mech. Eng.* **78**, 655 (1956).

THE STUDY OF TARS OBTAINED IN FLUIDIZED CARBONIZATION

By G. H. Watson and A. Fowler Williams

Coal Research Establishment, National Coal Board, Great Britain

Summary—A detailed study was made of the tar and liquor which were produced in high yield by the carbonization of a high-volatile, noncoking coal (Binley 9-ft. seam, rank code number 902, volatile matter 42% dry ash-free basis) in a bed fluidized by steam at 650°C in a 2-inch carbonizer.

The tar was separated into phenols, bases, and neutral oil by extraction with alkali and acid respectively. A similar separation was made on an ether extract of the aqueous liquor. Phenols were examined by fractional distillation; the neutral oil was studied by elution chromatography and measurement of a number of properties of the chromatographed fractions, including absorption spectra.

The tar contained 3·0% bases, 0·2% phenol, 2·4% cresols, 0·8% xylenols, 0·8% catechol and 15·7% other high-boiling phenols. In addition there was a significant quantity of lower-boiling phenols in the liquor.

The neutral oil, some 70% of which boiled above 350°C, contained not more than 10% of paraffins and cycloparaffins, about 20% of alkylated polynuclear aromatic hydrocarbons and at least 30% of oxygenated compounds in which C = O and OH groupings were identified. The remaining 40% was not examined in detail but was likely to be aromatic in nature and to contain oxygen in complex structures.

Résumé—Une étude détaillée a été faite du goudron et des eaux qui ont été produits, avec un rendement élevé, au cours de la carbonisation, dans un appareil de carbonisation de 2 pouces (50 mm) d'un charbon non cokéfiant à forte teneur en matières volatiles (Couche de 9 pieds Binley, No de code de rang 902, matières volatiles 42% exempt de cendres et d'eau), dans un lit fluidisé par de la vapeur à 650°C.

Le goudron fut séparé en phénols, bases et huile neutre par extraction au moyen, respectivement, d'alcali et d'acide. Une séparation analogue fut faite sur un extrait à l'éther de la liqueur aqueuse. Les phénols furent étudiés par distillation fractionnée; l'huile neutre fut étudiée par chromatographie par éluction et mesure d'un certain nombre de propriétés dont le spectre d'absorption des fractions de la chromatographie.

Le goudron contenait 3·0% de bases, 0·2% de phénol, 2·4% de crésols, 0·8% de xylénols, 0·8% de catéchol et 15·7% d'autres phénols à point d'ébullition élevé. En plus il y avait dans les eaux une quantité significative de phénols à bas point d'ébullition.

L'huile neutre, dont environ 70% bouillaient à environ 350°C ne contenait pas plus de 10% de paraffine et de cycloparaffine, environ 20% d'hydrocarbures aromatiques polynucléaires alkylatés et au moins 30% de composés oxygénés dans lesquels les groupes C = O et OH ont été identifiés. Les 40% restant n'ont pas été étudiés en détail, mais ils étaient vraisemblablement de nature aromatique et devaient contenir de l'oxygène dans des structures complexes.

Zusammenfassung—Der Aufsatz berichtet über eingehende Untersuchungen des Teeres und des wässrigen Kondensates, die in erheblichen Mengen bei der Schwelung einer hochflüchtigen, nicht kokenden Kohle (aus dem 2·70 m-Flöz der Zeche Binley, 42% flüchtige Bestandteile (waf), Ziffer 902 der Britischen Kohleklassifikation) im Wirbelbett anfielen. Gewirbelt wurde mit Dampf (650°C), die Versuchsapparatur hatte einen Ø von 5 cm.

Der Teer wurde durch Extraktion mit Alkali oder Säuren in Phenole, Basen und Neutral-Öle geschieden. Einer gleichen Scheidung wurden die aus dem wässrigen Kondensat mit Äther extrahierten organischen Bestandteile unterzogen. Die Phenole wurden dann durch fraktionierte Destillation untersucht. Das Neutral-Öl wurde unter Anwendung der Eluierungstechnik chromatographisch untersucht; verschiedene Eigenschaften der chromatographischen Fraktionen wurden gemessen und die gewonnenen Ergebnisse durch spektroskopische Untersuchungen ergänzt.

Der Teer enthielt 3% Basen, 0·2% Phenole, 2·4% Kresole, 0·8% Xylenole, 0·8% Brenzkatechin und 15·7% sonstige hochsiedende Phenole. Dazu kam eine erhebliche Menge von niedriger siedenden Phenolen im wässrigen Kondensat.

Das Neutral-Öl setzte sich zu rd. 70% aus Fraktionen mit einem Siedepunkt über 350°C zusammen. Es enthielt nur 10% Paraffine und Zyklo-Paraffine, etwa 20% alkylierte aromatische Hydrocarbone mit mehreren Ringen und mindestens 30% Sauerstoff-Verbindungen, in denen C=O und OH-Gruppen festgestellt wurden. Die restlichen 40% wurden nicht eingehender untersucht; es ist anzunehmen, dass sie aromatisch sind und Sauerstoff in komplizierten Strukturen enthalten.

I. INTRODUCTION

THE pollution of the atmosphere by the smoke from coal fires is a matter of grave national concern. One of the most serious causes of the nuisance is the burning of bituminous coal on the domestic open grate. The National Coal Board is therefore conducting research into ways of increasing the supply of solid reactive smokeless fuels for domestic use. The main object is to devise economic methods of processing the more readily available low-rank, high-volatile, noncoking coals, which are unsuitable for making either coke or other smokeless fuels by established processes.

An essential stage in any process for the production of smokeless fuel is the devolatilization or partial devolatilization of the coal used. One promising line of approach is the carbonization of coal at low temperature in a fluidized bed. This technique offers the advantages of high heat and mass transfer, ease of handling solids and very high throughput per unit of reaction space, with consequent savings in capital, labour and energy costs.

At the Coal Research Establishment of the National Coal Board an investigation into the possibilities and potentialities of the fluidized carbonization of high-volatile coals was begun by carbonizing a few coals from the Midlands in a small two-inch fluidized carbonizer. The experiments were made primarily to study the behaviour of the coals and the operation of the plant. The quantity of tar from any one run was insufficient for a detailed examination, and it was possible to measure only the total content of phenols, bases and neutral material. This was done by dissolving the tar in benzene, filtering off the benzene-insoluble material, and removing the phenols and bases from the soluble portion by washing with dilute alkali and acid—a procedure necessitated by the high viscosity of the tar.

Some typical analyses are shown in Table 1.

TABLE 1

Analysis of Tar from the 2 in. Fluidized Carbonizer
Coal: Binley, Nine Feet. C.R.C.: 902
Fluidizing Medium: Nitrogen
%s wt. on dry tar

Average temp. of carbonization (°C)	Sp. gr. of dry tar 15·5°/15·5°C	Entrained coal + " free carbon "	Benzene-insoluble tar	Tar acids	Bases	Neutral oil	Tarry residues*
500	1·090	0·8	5·2	25·5	2·2	54·5	11·8
600	1·090	0·5	7·8	26·3	1·7	54·5	9·2
650	1·087	0·7	4·4	27·3	1·9	60·5	5·2

* These compounds were not an inherent feature of the tar but were produced during the extraction processes, mainly during the caustic-alkali extraction stage.

The carbonization experiments showed that a very high yield of tar was to be expected from the fluidized carbonization at low temperature of high-volatile coal. The tar would have a high content of phenols (20% to 25%), but, as shown later, would contain a large proportion of high-boiling material.

It was clear that, if fluidized carbonization were ultimately practised on a large scale, very large quantities of tar would be made for which the most profitable means of disposal would have to be found. In fact, the economic stability of the process might be critically influenced by the establishment of a satisfactory and permanent market for the byproducts.

It was supposed that the tars produced by the fluidized carbonization of low-rank, high-volatile coals would in many respects be novel in character, and much research would be needed to find methods of processing them to the best advantage. The first step was a thorough elucidation of the nature of the tar. This required much more material than had hitherto been available. To obtain this in a single run would have been possible only on larger carbonizing apparatus than the two-inch carbonizer in use, and although plans for building such apparatus had been prepared, it had not been built. Therefore a succession of runs was made with a characteristic coal and under typical conditions of carbonization with the sole object of obtaining tar for examination. Although twenty runs were devoted to this purpose, the total quantity of tar collected was only about 2 kg, since each run produced only about 100 g tar.

The aim of the work was the elucidation of the main chemical types and structures present in the tar, as far as possible as it was produced in the carbonizer. This qualification is important, since the tar was known to be labile and to undergo change if subjected to heat. Obviously, a complete examination could not be achieved; the tar was too complex a mixture and too small a quantity of it was available. The latter restriction also imposed limitations on the technique adopted in some parts of the investigation. It was hoped, however, that the work would give an insight into the nature of the tar and would pinpoint the main difficulties likely to be encountered in any subsequent examination; in short, the work would provide a basis for extended investigations in the future.

II. EXPERIMENTAL

1. *Raw Material*

The coal carbonized in the succession of runs to provide the 2 kg of tar for examination was from the Binley Nine Feet seam, coal rank code number 902, volatile matter 42% (dry ash-free basis). The conditions of carbonization were: temperature 650°C; fluidizing medium, steam; average time of residence in the reactor, 20 minutes.

The yield of tar obtained during these runs represented about 24 gallons per ton of coal charged to the carbonizer. One factor, however, must be noted. When the runs were made, the tar condensing and collecting system attached to the carbonizing unit had not been perfected, and an appreciable proportion of the tar was lost. In view of this loss, it is emphasized that the distribution of components reported herein refers to the tar as collected and may not necessarily be representative of that in the tar as produced. Nevertheless, it was felt that this did not detract from the value of any information gained concerning the nature of the tar collected.

Produced with the tar was a quantity of aqueous liquor equivalent to about 86 gallons per ton of coal carbonized. This is a very high yield, but much of the water was derived from the steam used for fluidization. The liquor was of interest on account of the phenols it contained, and it is considered later in this paper in connection with the phenols present in the tar.

Before beginning the main investigation, a small sample of the tar was examined by a straight Engler distillation. There were marked signs of cracking at an overhead temperature of about 300°C. The content of phenols and bases in fractions of the distillate was measured by washing with dilute alkali and acid. The results are shown in Table 2. It is noteworthy that the tar was high boiling in nature and that naphthalene was absent from the fraction boiling in the range 210°C to 230°C.

TABLE 2

Straight Distillation of the Crude Tar
Distillation Rate: 2 ml per minute

Boiling range of fraction (°C)	Apprx. Sp. gr.	Condition after 4 hr at 15·5°C	Wt. on dry, coal -free tar (%)	10% NaOH-extract		10% H₂SO₄-extract		Relative density of neutral fraction D_4 20°C
				% wt. on fraction	% wt. on dry, coal -free tar	% wt. on fraction	% wt. on. dry, coal -free tar	
108–210	0·90	Yellow oil	2·2	36·6	0·8	3·1	0·07	
210–230	0·93	Greenish-yellow oil	3·9	46·4	1·8	5·1	0·2	0·91
230–270	1·0	Greenish-brown oil	10·7	53·0	5·7	3·2	0·3	0·94
270–300	1·0	Red-brown oil	17·9	35·8	6·4	3·5	0·6	0·98
300–end	1·0	Red-brown waxy oil	21·4	27·0	5·8	3·2	0·7	0·99
Residue from distillation		Pitch coke	35·2 (less coal)					
Loss on distillation			8·7*					

* This loss is probably due to uncondensed gases produced during the cracking stage.

2. *Separation into Main Chemical Types*

The tar was first separated into three main divisions, phenols, bases and neutral material. The method developed for the assay of the small samples of tar referred to above was used for this purpose. The technique is outlined schematically in Fig. 1. Briefly, the tar was dissolved in benzene and the benzene-insoluble portion removed. The insoluble portion was further separated with alcohol into tar and entrained coal (some 11% on dry tar). It will be noted that the coal content of the tar was higher than had been observed in previous small samples (compare Table 1).

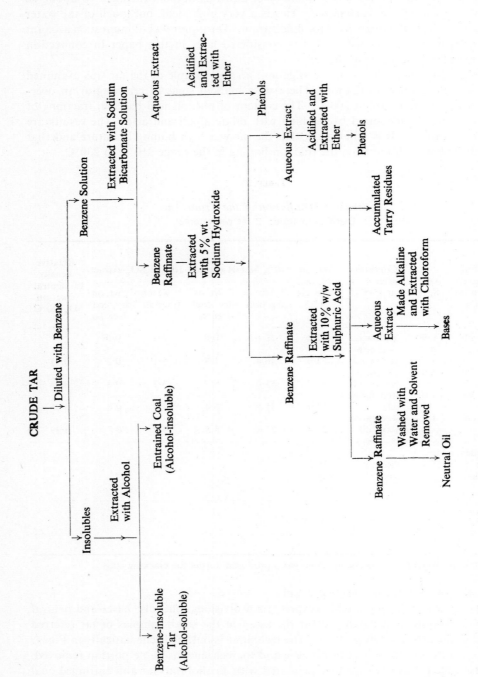

Fig. 1—Scheme of separation of the tar into main chemical types

The benzene solution (291) was washed batchwise in glass separating funnels with alkali (saturated bicarbonate solution followed by 5% wt. caustic soda solution) and mineral acid (10% w/w sulphuric acid) so as to separate the phenols and bases from the neutral oil. In order to free the aqueous extracts from nonphenolic or non-basic material, which properly belonged to the benzene raffinate, each extract was backwashed with benzene before further treatment. The bicarbonate and caustic solutions were " sprung " with hydrochloric acid, and the phenols (about 40 g and 300 g respectively) recovered separately by extraction with ether; the acid extract was neutralized with strong caustic-soda solution and the liberated bases (about 50 g) recovered in chloroform. The final raffinate was washed with water and the benzene stripped from the neutral oil (about 700 g) in a 40-plate fractionating column. The yields of the various products are shown in Table 3.

TABLE 3

Separation of the Crude Tar into Chemical Types
%s wt. on dry tar

Component	Wt. on tar (as received) (%)	Wt. on tar (coal-free basis) (%)
Entrained coal	11·2	—
Benzene-insoluble tar	12·0	13·5
Phenols extracted by sodium bicarbonate solution	2·2	2·5
Phenols not extracted by sodium bicarbonate, extracted by caustic soda solution	15·4	17·3
Bases	2·7	3·0
Neutral oil	40·4	45·5
Tarry residues	10·8	12·2
Working loss	5·3	

During the separation of the tar, some 12% of the tar was converted into insoluble residues, mainly during the caustic-soda extraction. It is likely that these residues were produced by oxidation of some of the phenols present in the tar by air in the presence of alkali. The benzene-insoluble portion of the tar, being freely soluble in alcohol, may also have arisen from complex tar phenols. None of these residues were examined further in the present work.

Investigations of the acids and neutral material are now described in sequence. As for the bases present in the tar, these were shown to be high boiling in nature but in view of the small quantity available and their likely complexity, they were not examined further.

3. *Examination of Tar Phenols*

The phenols removed from the tar by bicarbonate solution and by caustic soda solution were examined separately by the usual methods. Briefly, the mixtures were distilled under vacuum to remove pitch-forming constituents and then fractionated into small cuts. For the bicarbonate extract, an 8-plate column (6 cm × 0·6 cm i.d. packed with 1/16-in. Dixon gauze rings) was used and for the caustic-soda extract, a 25-plate column (40 cm × 1·4 cm i.d. packed with 1/16-in. Dixon gauze rings) fitted with a Simons-type, vapour-off-take head.[1] This type of head was used, since only a relatively small quantity of phenols was being fractionated, and it was necessary to provide for as small a holdup as possible.

The common types of phenols were shown by chemical tests to be present in the low-boiling fractions. Phenol was identified by the formation of phenoxyacetic acid,[2] *o*-cresol by formation of its complex with cineole,[3] and *m*-cresol by preparation of the trinitro derivative.[4] The amounts of these and higher phenols (C_6, C_7, C_8, and C_9 phenols) present in the tar were assessed from the measured hydroxyl values.[5] On distillation, about one third of the bicarbonate extract yielded solid-containing fractions. These solids were recrystallized from a mixture of light petroleum

TABLE 4

The Composition of the Acidic Portion of the Tar

Component	Wt. on bicarb.-extractable material (%)	Wt. on caustic-extractable material (%)	Approx. wt. % on dry tar (coal-free basis)			Yield on coal carbonized (lb./ton)
			From the bicarb. extract	From the caustic extract	Total yield of phenols on tar	
Phenol	1·3	1·2	0·03	0·22	0·2	0·5
Orthocresol		7·2		1·25		
Metacresol	} 4·9	} 6·1	} 0·12	} 1·05	} 2·4	} 5·8
Paracresol						
Xylenols	4·4	3·7	0·11	0·64	0·8	1·9
Higher phenols boiling below 220°C (propyl phenols, methyl ethyl phenols, etc.)		4·6		0·8	0·8	1·9
High-boiling alkyl phenols	9·4	8·8	0·24	1·54	1·8	4·3
Catechol	33·8		0·85		0·8	1·9
Unidentified dihydric phenols	3·8		0·10		0·1	0·2
High-boiling tar acids, (distilled, translucent red resin)		24·4		4·23	4·2	1·0
Unexamined distillation residues (high-boiling tar acids)	42·4	44·0	1·07	7·65	8·8	21·2
Total	100·0	100·0	2·52	17·38	19·9	38·7

and benzene and were found to consist almost entirely of catechol (identified by mixed melting point formation of the picrate derivative and X-ray examination).

The results are shown in Table 4. From this table, it is seen that less than a quarter of all the phenols consisted of the more valuable, lower-boiling phenols, and the amount of phenol was very small. Despite this, the total yield of cresols and xylenols boiling below 220°C, based on the quantity of coal carbonized, was higher than that from coke-oven tar.

It is appropriate here to refer to the aqueous liquor which accompanied the tar. The organic matter was extracted from this with ether and separated into acidic, basic and neutral substances with alkali and acid. The acidic portion was analysed in a manner similar to that already described for the phenols from the tar. The results are given in Table 5. This table shows that about one fifth of the liquor acids consisted of low-boiling, monohydric phenols, and about one third of the dihydric phenol, catechol.

TABLE 5

Examination of the Acids in the Liquor

Component	Wt. on liquor (as received basis)	Yield on coal carbonized (lb./ton)
Acids	1·6	13·8
Aliphatic carboxylic acids (propionic acid type)	0·10	0·9
Phenol	0·12	1·0
Cresols	0·20	1·7
Xylenols	0·03	0·2
Catechol	0·42	3·6
Catechol-bearing oil	0·18	1·6
Undistilled and unexamined residue	0·55	4·8
Bases	0·005	0·04
Neutral oil	0·02	0·15

One point of interest is the comparatively high yield of catechol that was extracted from the tar by sodium bicarbonate solution. On the basis of coal carbonized, the amount of catechol extracted from the tar was approximately one half of that obtained from the liquor.

It should also be noted that the phenols in the liquor are a significant proportion of the total quantity of phenols produced during carbonization.

4. *Neutral Oil*

The first step in the examination of the neutral oil was to separate it into small fractions. This was done in two stages. Chromatography was used to split up the oil, predominantly according to molecular type. The resulting chromatographed fractions were further simplified by fractional distillation.

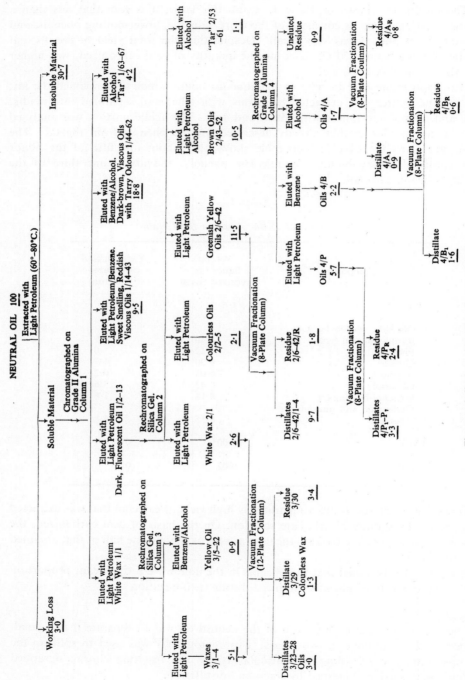

Figures underlined are yields (% wt.) on neutral oil.

Fig. 2—Scheme of examination of the neutral oil

The scheme of examination is illustrated in Fig. 2 which gives the reference numbers and yields of the various fractions collected. Details of the chromatographic and fractionating columns used are given in the Appendix.

The oil (505 g) was extracted with light petroleum and the solution chromatographed on a column of alumina (Grade II activation as measured by the Brockman and Schodder dye test[6] using the technique of elution development. The column was developed successively with light petroleum, benzene, chloroform, and alcohol. Solvent was removed from fractions of the eluate by warming in a slow stream of oxygen-free nitrogen. The initial fractions of the light petroleum eluate were waxy; the remainder gave rise to fluorescent, mobile oils. Other fractions off the alumina column ranged from mobile oils to reddish-brown, translucent gums and finally, a black tar. The wax (30 g) was rechromatographed on silica gel using light petroleum as developing solvent. The fluorescent oils (154·8 g) were bulked and also rechromatographed on silica gel using light petroleum and then alcohol as developers. From this column, more of the white wax was separated, and it was followed by light-coloured mobile oils, dark-coloured viscous oils and finally by a tar. The dark-coloured oils (39·4 g) were rechromatographed on a column of Grade I[6] alumina, light petroleum, benzene and alcohol being used as developers. The reddish gums (143 g) were not rechromatographed.

After examination (as described below), the solvent-free fractions were bulked and fractionally distilled (using 8- or 12-plate[7] packed columns) mainly according to their physical properties and to the quantity of sample available. The distillate fractions were examined in the same way as the parent chromatographic fractions.

The fractions from both chromatography and distillation were examined with a Hilger "Uvispek", ultra-violet spectrophotometer and a Grubb-Parsons double-beam, infra-red spectrometer fitted with a rock-salt prism. The information sought by spectroscopic examination included (a) the presence or otherwise of aromatic substances, (b) the size of the aromatic nuclei, if present, (c) the ratio of aromatic CH groups to nonaromatic CH groups, (d) the presence and type of oxygen-containing groups.

To facilitate and extend the spectroscopic evidence, use was made, where possible, of correlations that have been proposed between refractive index, density, molecular weight[8] and the structure of hydrocarbons. These correlations are (a) the graphical correlation between specific refraction, molecular weight and percentage carbon in naphthene rings which van Nes and van Westen[9] have compiled for saturated hydrocarbons, and (b) the correlation described by Hersh et al.[10] for condensed aromatic ring systems (alkyl benzenes, alkyl naphthalenes, etc.), which relates refractive index, molecular weight, number of aromatic rings per molecule and the weight per cent of rings.

Specimen data are given in Tables 6 to 9.

It can be calculated from the boiling range of the chromatographed fractions given in Table 6 that some 70% of the neutral oil boils above 350°C.

It was possible to arrange the fractions broadly into a few groups according to the relative power of retention on the chromatographic columns. These groups are given in Table 10 and are discussed in more detail below in the order in which they were eluted from the columns.

Table 6
Chromatography of the Neutral Oil

Grade II alumina column 1	Silica gel column 2	Silica gel column 3	Grade I alumina column 4	Cum. wt. on neutral oil (%)	% wt. C	% wt. H	% wt. O (by diff.)	Mol. wt.	Refractive index 20°C n_D	Relative density 20°C D_4	Specific dispersion	Av. no. of rings per mol.	Av. wt. of rings (%)	Up to 250°C	250°C to 300°C	300°C to 350°C	Above 350°C
1/1		3/1			83·6	13·5	2·9	325	1·4551	0·834	97	2·0N	42N				
		3/2						290	1·4561	0·826	103		33				
		3/3						290	1·4571	0·825	102		29				
		3/4		5·1													
		3/5 to 22		6·0													
	2/1			8·6	85·1	13·7	1·2	335	1·4571	0·835	95	2·0N	40N	9·0	10·0	17·0	64·0
	2/2 –5			10·7										31·0	11·0	18·0	40·0
	2/6			11·6	83·8	11·0	5·2	355	1·490			1·4A	27·6A				
	2/7 –32			19·9													
	2/33–36			20·9	86·5	8·4	5·1	271	1·5768 to 1·5898			2·5A	55·2				
1/2 to 1/13	2/37–38			21·4													
	2/39–42			22·2	87·0	7·6	5·4	270	1·6028 to 1·6089			2·7A	60·0	20·9	21·8	14·8	42·5
	2/43 to 52		4/P	27·9	87·9	7·8	4·3	340						3·5	5·3	36·8	54·4
			4/B	30·1	87·0	7·05	5·95	340									
			4/A	31·8	79·6	8·6	11·80	400									
	Residues			33·8													
1/14–17				34·8	85·9	8·2	5·9	280									
1/18–43				43·3										7·4	4·2	4·2	84·2
1/44				43·6	84·5	8·0	7·5	320									
1/45–61				54·8													
1/62				62·1	78·6	8·3	13·1	385						3·2	12·7	7·4	76·7
1/63–67				66·3													
Unchromatographed residue				97·0													94·0
Working Loss				100·0													

N = Naphthenic rings
A = Aromatic rings

TABLE 7

Fractional Distillation of Wax Fractions (Ref. 3/1—4+2/1)

Fraction ref.	Appearance at room temperature	Yield frac. Wt. on parent fraction (%)	Boiling range calc'd. for 760 mm (°C)	Refractive index of distillates		Mol. wt.	Approximate no. of C atoms in paraffin known to occur in given boiling range
				at 40°C	at 20°C		
3/1		2·7	155–239	1·4318	1·4351		$C_9 - C_{14}$
3/2	Light-brown oil	5·5	239–245	1·4345	1·4405	200	
3/3	Colourless oil	5·1	245–280	1·4373	1·4428	225	$C_{14} - C_{16}$
3/4	Colourless oil	11·3	280–305	1·4402	1·4462	270	$C_{16} - C_{18}$
3/5	Brown oil	8·1	305–320	1·4445	1·4501	285	$C_{18} - C_{19}$
3/6	Pale-yellow oil	6·4	320–340	1·4473	1·4523	310	$C_{19} - C_{20}$
3/7	Colourless wax	16·8	340–380	1·4500		310	$C_{20} - C_{23}$
3/8	Dark-brown wax (residue)	44·1				390	

a) *The wax fractions—ref. 3/1 to 3/4 and 2/1 (7·7% wt. on the neutral oil).* The values of the specific dispersion (95 to 103) lie within the limits given by Darmois[11] for mixtures of paraffins and naphthenes. The values of the specific refraction (0·325 to 0·330) are also of the same order as those for mixtures of paraffins and naphthenes, whose molecular weights range from 290 to 330, given by Eisenlohr.[12] Spectroscopic examination showed that aromatic rings were absent, that the waxes were predominantly saturated, and that carbon chains containing not less than six methylene ($-CH_2-$) groups per molecule were present. There was also evidence for a small amount of unsaturation in the form of cis- and trans-olefin types, $RCH = HR$ and $RCH = CH_2$. The amount of this type of unsaturation decreased with increasing boiling point. It should be noted that if an appreciable amount of unsaturation were present in the waxes, the values of the specific dispersion would have been much higher than were actually observed.

The values of the molecular weight indicate that the waxes contain, on average, C_{20} to C_{24} molecules, though the values of the refractive indices are higher than those of the appropriate paraffins, e.g. *n*-eicosane (C_{20}; m.p. 36·4°C; b.p. 340°C; $n\text{D}^{50°C}$ 1·4307) and *n*-tetracosane (C_{24}; m.p. 51·1°C; b.p. 390°C; $n\text{D}^{65°C}$

Table 8

Fractional Distillation of the Light Petroleum Eluate from Silica Gel (Ref. Fractions 2/6—42)

Fraction Reference	Appearance	Yield Frac. Wt. on parent fraction (%)	Boiling Range Calculated for 760 mm (°C)	Refractive Index $n_D^{20°C}$	Relative density $D_4^{20°C}$	Specific Dispersion	Ultimate Analysis			Mol. Wt.	Average Number of Aromatic Rings	Wt. % of Aromatic Rings
							% wt. C	% wt. H	% wt. O (by diff.)			
2/6-42/1	Brownish yellow oil	20·8	175–254°	1·5633	0·983	219	86·2	7·85	5·95	165	1·7	69
2/6-42/2	–do–	22·2	254–307°	1·5782	1·001	231	87·2	8·15	4·65	190	2·0	67
2/6-42/3	–do–	22·4	307–380°	1·5814	1·016	224	87·5	8·55	3·95	220	2·2	62
2/6-42/4	–do–	19·1	380–420°	1·567	1·011	178	87·5	9·70	2·80	300	2·4	49
2/6-42/R	Residue (Pitch)	15·5 (by diff.)	>420°									

TABLE 9

Fractional Distillation of the Eluates from Grade I Alumina (Ref. Fractions 4/P, 4/B, 4/A)

Fraction Reference	Yield Frac. % Wt. on parent fraction	Boiling Range Calculated for 760 mm (°C)	Refractive Index $n_D^{20°C}$	Relative Density $D_4^{20°C}$	Specific Dispersion	Ultimate Analysis of Distillates % wt. C	% wt. H	% wt. (by diff.) O	Mol. Wt.	Average Number of Aromatic Rings	Aromatic Rings (%wt)
4/P_1	2·2	199–237	1·5485			81·5	8·10	10·4	160		
4/P_2	3·8	237–279	1·581			85·2	7·25	7·55	220		
4/P_3	3·2	279–307	1·604			87·5	7·10	5·40	220		
4/P_4	11·0	307–322	1·617	1·069	266	87·7	7·00	5·30	200		
4/P_5	19·0	322–336	1·631	1·075	263	89·0	7·30	3·70	215	2·6	73·7
4/P_6	7·4	336–359	1·636			88·6	7·55	3·85	210		
4/P_7	10·2	359–407	1·637	1·080	290	88·4	7·25	4·35	210	2·7	79·7
4/P_R	43·2	>407									
4/B_1	72·0	312–480	1·652	1·109	325	87·7	7·00	5·3	220		
4/B_R	28·0	>480									
4/A_1	55·0	280–530	1·560	1·046	162	80·8	8·75	10·45	440		
4/A_R	45·0	>530									

H

TABLE 10

Properties of the Chromatographed Fractions of the Neutral Oil

Nature of the fraction	Frac. % wt. on the neutral oil	Observations on the fractions
Wax (Eluted from silica gel and from Grade II alumina with light petroleum)	7·7	Aromatic rings absent. Consists mainly of paraffins and cycloparaffins. At least 40% appears to exist as paraffins in which the number of carbon atoms per molecule varies widely. (The paraffin, $C_{29}H_{60}$, was obtained by recrystallization). It is likely that dicyclic naphthenes or homologues thereof are also present.
Interfraction (Colourless oil eluted from silica gel with light petroleum)	2·1	This fraction was not examined in detail. It is likely to contain both paraffinic and aromatic structures which would be separated by further chromatography.
Hydrocarbon oils: (Eluted from silica gel with light petroleum)	11·5	Consists mainly of alkylated naphthalenes. Single- and three-membered ring aromatic hydrocarbons also present, together with a small amount of olefinic unsaturation. Some C = O groups (possibly a quinone structure) may be present but the amount in any particular fraction decreases with its boiling point.
(Eluted from Grade I alumina with light petroleum)	5·7	At least 80% of this fraction appears to consist of alkylated naphthalenes and aromatic hydrocarbons containing three, four and possibly more rings. Aromatic structures with attached CO groups may also be present in compounds boiling below 320°C.
(Eluted from Grade I alumina with benzene)	2·2	Predominantly aromatic hydrocarbons containing three rings per molecule. Some CO groups present.
Compounds of high oxygen content. (Eluted from Grade I alumina with alcohol)	1·7	Contains aromatic structures—predominantly benzene and naphthalene rings—with CO and OH groups present also.
Reddish-brown viscous oils or gums (eluted from Grade II alumina with chloroform-alcohol mixtures)	28·3	Aromatic structures and CO groups (aldehydes, quinones or ketones) present throughout. The increasing oxygen content of the fractions as they came off the chromatographic column (5·9% wt. in the first 1% (on neutral oil) to 13·1% wt. in the last 7·3% wt.) can, in part, be attributed to an increasing content of CO groups and also to the presence of OH groups (hindered phenols or alcohols or both) in the later fractions. No olefinic unsaturation present.
Unexamined residues	37·8	Hydroxyl (OH) groups present in the portion insoluble in light petroleum (30·7% wt.).
Working loss	3·0	

1·4303). On the basis of the available evidence therefore, it is likely that the waxes contain some naphthenic structures. If they are wholly saturated, the van Nes—van Westen relationship gives the number of naphthenic rings per molecule as about 2; this means that the waxes are composed either of homologues of dicyclic naphthenes or are physical mixtures of dicyclic naphthenes and paraffins. Support for this conclusion is given by the observed value of the H/C (atomic) ratio (1·92), this being 1·8 in the case of a dicyclic naphthene and 2·2 for a paraffin containing an equal number of carbon atoms. The van Nes—van Westen relationship also shows that about 40% of wax fractions 3/1 and 2/1 consists of naphthenic rings.

From this picture of the wax molecules, the value of the average molecular weight in one particular sample chosen for further examination would require about 32 carbon atoms in the aliphatic chains. X-ray examination of a sample of this wax fraction, after recrystallization from benzene, showed that the paraffin, n-nonacosane, $C_{29}H_{60}$, was in fact present. The X-ray result also means that the chains do not wholly exist in substituted naphthenes, but some must be present as free paraffins.

From the examination of the wax distillates (see Table 7), it would seem likely that these fractions arise from the paraffinic portions of the parent wax. Considerations of boiling points in conjunction with molecular weights indicate that the molecular chain length ranges from C_9 in the first fraction to C_{23} in the final distillate. This is in agreement with the spectroscopic evidence for the succeeding fraction (i.e. the residue), that chains containing not less than 19 carbon atoms are present per molecule.

b) The light petroleum eluate from silica gel—ref. oil fractions 2/6 to 2/42 (11·5%wt. on the neutral oil). Spectroscopic examination gave evidence of the occurrence of some separation according to molecular size during the chromatography. Thus in fraction 2/6, single-ring aromatics predominated and monosubstituted, meta- and para-disubstituted structures were identified; in fractions removed from the column later (2/33—36), fused-ring aromatic structures predominated. Small amounts of cis- and trans-olefinic unsaturation was identified in both samples, though they were less in amount in the more highly adsorbed fraction.

This general picture was confirmed by the Hersh ring analysis which indicated that the number of aromatic rings per molecule was 1·4 in sample 2/6 (wt. % of aromatic rings, 27·6), and 2·5 in sample 2/33—36 (wt. % of aromatic rings, 55·2).

The infra-red spectra of the distillates (ref. 2/6—42/1—4) were characteristic of substituted aromatic hydrocarbons, the number of rings per molecule and the degree of substitution increasing with increase in boiling point. The aromatic structures ranged from substituted benzenes and naphthalenes in the first fraction, boiling 175°C to 250°C (Hersh; $R_A = 1·7$, wt. % of aromatic rings, 69) to three-ring structures and higher in the fourth fraction, boiling 380°C to 420°C ($R_A = 2·4$, wt. % of aromatic rings, 49). Ultimate analysis indicated the presence of some oxygen in the distillates, the amount decreasing with the boiling range. The spectroscopic evidence for the presence of oxygen was inconclusive, though the decrease in oxygen content might be associated with the decrease in intensity of a " shoulder " at 1640 cm⁻¹, arising possibly from a carbonyl (quinone) grouping.

c) The light petroleum eluate from Grade I alumina, ref. oil fraction, 4/P. (5·7%wt. on neutral oil). Spectroscopic examination of the distillates from this material showed that the average number of rings per molecule increased with increase in boiling point from substituted benzenes in the first fraction (b.r. 200°C to 240°C), to substituted benzenes and naphthalenes in the next fraction (b.r. 240°C to 280°C), and substituted naphthalenes and three-ring structures in the last fraction (b.r. 305°C to 320°C). Two types of CO groupings were present in each of these fractions, but the suggested presence of tetralone or benzophenone in the first of them was not borne out by examination of the pure compounds.

The infra-red spectra of the fifth and higher boiling fractions were characteristic of substituted aromatic compounds and similar to those of the earlier fractions, ref. 2/6—42/1—4. Oxygen groupings could not be detected in these fractions even though ultimate analysis indicated an oxygen content of 3% to 4%. It would seem reasonable, therefore, to apply the Hersh analysis to what seems to be, essentially, a mixture of condensed ring aromatic hydrocarbons. For the fifth fraction (b.r. 320°C to 340°C), R_A would appear to be 2·6, and the weight per cent of aromatic rings, 73·7% (substituted naphthalenes or fluorenes). Likewise for the seventh fraction (b.r. 360°C to 400°C), R_A was calculated as 2·7 and the weight per cent of rings 79·7% (substituted anthracenes or phenanthrenes).

The most perhaps that can be said about this fraction is that at least 80% would appear to consist of substituted naphthalenes and other aromatic hydrocarbons containing three, four and possibly more rings.

d) *The benzene eluate from Grade I alumina—ref. oil fraction 4/B (2·2% wt. on neutral oil).* Ultra-violet examination indicated that three-ring aromatics were present in the distillate b.r. 310°C to 480°C with some CO groups in two types of structures. From considerations of the boiling point one might expect four membered ring structures to be present also.

e) *Fractions of high oxygen content.* It must be emphasized that in view of their chromatographic history, one might expect fractions 2/6—42, 4/P and 4/B to consist solely of aromatic hydrocarbons. The presence of oxygen, as indicated by ultimate analysis, and the identification of CO groups in the lower-boiling distillates by spectroscopic examination complicates the ring analyses, but it is not felt to militate against the main conclusions.

The following two fractions, which were strongly adsorbed on the chromatographic column, contained a significantly higher proportion of oxygen than the preceding fractions.

(i) The alcohol eluate from Grade I alumina—ref. oil fraction 4/A (1·7% wt. on neutral oil): spectroscopic examination indicated that substituted naphthalenes and benzenes were present in the fraction b.r. 300°C to 500°C, and that the higher degree of adsorption on the chromatographic column was due to the presence of OH groups (hindered phenols or alcohols) as well as CO groups.

(ii) The chloroform-alcohol eluate from Grade II alumina—ref. reddish-brown viscous oils or gums, 1/14 to 1/62 (28·3% wt. on neutral oil): spectroscopic examination indicated that aromatic structures were present throughout with no olefinic unsaturation. The increase in oxygen content shown by ultimate analysis can be related to the increase in the amount of CO groupings present in fractions of increasing degree of adsorption on the column and also to the appearance of OH groups (alcohols and possibly hindered phenols also) in these later fractions.

III. CONCLUSIONS

a) The relatively high proportion of phenols is an important feature of the tar, although the amount of ordinary phenol in it was only about 0·2% and the amount of potentially useful phenols (boiling below 220°C) only about 4%. In addition, however, there was a significant quantity of the lower-boiling phenols in the liquor. Thus the total yield of phenol was 1·5 lb per ton of coal carbonized, of which 1·0 lb./ton was in the liquor; the total yield of cresols was 7·5 lb./ton of coal carbonized, of which 1·7 lb/ton was in the liquor. The yield of catechol was 1·9 lb/ton from the tar and 3·6 lb/ton from the liquor.

The bulk of the phenols was high boiling in nature, for which the market would be uncertain and low priced. The value of these higher phenols would be greatly increased if they could be converted in high yield to lower-boiling products.

b) The neutral oil in the sample of tar examined contained not more than about 10% of paraffins and cycloparaffins. The structure of the remainder was essentially aromatic, about 20% comprising hydrocarbons and a further 30% comprising so-called oxygenated compounds. The 35% or so of the neutral oil, which was insoluble in light petroleum and therefore not examined, is almost certainly likely to be aromatic in nature and to contain oxygen groupings in complex structures.

c) About 40% of the nonaromatic hydrocarbons consisted of liquid paraffins, ranging in carbon number from C_9 to C_{20} approximately, and 60% of hydrocarbon waxes of a higher number of carbon atoms. The hydrocarbon, $C_{29}H_{60}$, was isolated from these waxes, in which the presence of dicyclic naphthenes was also suspected.

d) No solid aromatic hydrocarbons, e.g. naphthalene, acenaphthene, etc., such as are found in high-temperature tars and to a lesser extent in vertical retort tars, were detected in the "fluidized" tar. The aromatic-hydrocarbon portion of this tar consisted essentially of oily compounds, some 50% being mainly of the alkylated naphthalenes type. The remainder of these hydrocarbons comprised alkyl-substituted aromatics containing from one to at least four rings per molecule. These compounds separated on the chromatographic columns in the order of increasing nuclear size, decreasing substitution, increasing refractive index and decreasing atomic hydrogen to carbon ratio.

e) As chromatographed, the "aromatic oxygenated compounds" were reddish brown gummy substances but, on distillation, they yielded clear mobile oils. CO (ketonic, aldehydric or quinonoid) and OH groups (hindered phenols or alcohols) were identified in these structures by absorption spectroscopy.

f) As in the case of the phenols, a large proportion of the neutral oil was high boiling in nature (some 70% b.>350°C). Its market value would no doubt be considerably increased if it could be economically converted to lower-boiling material.

REFERENCES

1. Simons J. H., *Industr. Engng. Chem. (Anal.)*, **10**, 29 (1938).
2. Koelsch C. F., *J. Amer. chem. Soc.*, **53**, 304 (1931).

3. POTTER F. M., and WILLIAMS H. B., *J. Soc. chem. Ind., Lond.,* **51**, 59T (1932).
4. RASCHIG F., *Z. angew. Chem.,* **31**, 759 (1900).
5. BRUNNER H., and THOMAS H. R., *J. appl. Chem.,* **3**, 49 (1953).
6. BROCKMAN H., and SCHODDER H., *Ber. dtsch. chem. Ges.,* **74**, 73 (1941).
7. DIXON O. G., *J. Soc. chem. Ind. Lond.,* **68**, 299 (1949).
8. SUCHARDA E., and BOBRANSKI B., *Semi-micro Methods for the Elementary Analysis of Organic Compounds.* London, Gallenkamp (1936).
9. VAN NES K., and VAN WESTEN H. A., *Aspects of the Constitution of Mineral Oils,* p. 309, New York, Elsevier (1951).
10. HERSH R. E., *et al., J. Inst. Petrol.,* **36**, 624 (1950).
11. DARMOIS E., *Compt. rend.,* **171**, 952 (1920).
12. EISENLOHR F., *Z. phys. Chem.,* **75**, 594 (1910).

APPENDIX

DETAILS OF CHROMATOGRAPHIC AND FRACTIONATING COLUMNS

Neutral Oil: Weight of sample, 505 g.
Weight of light petroleum extract, 350 g.

Chromatographic Columns:

Column 1: (Downward elution)   3000 g of activated alumina (100—200 mesh, Grade II activation as measured by the Brockman and Schodder dye test), contained in a glass column measuring 138 cm × 5·5 cm i.d.
Adsorbent : sample wt. ratio = 8·6 : 1.

Column 2: (Downward elution)   2000 g of silica gel (100—120 mesh; specified acid free; heated for three hours at 100°C to 120°C before use) contained in a glass column. This column consisted of two sections, the upper one measuring 113 cm × 5·5 cm i.d. and the lower one 51 cm × 2·8 cm i.d.)
Adsorbent : sample wt. ratio = 13 : 1.

Column 3: (Downward elution)   550 g of silica gel (100—120 mesh, specified acid free, heated for three hours at 100°C to 120°C before use) contained in a graded glass column. This column consisted of three sections, the top section measuring 27·5 cm × 3·6 cm i.d., the middle section, 74·5 cm × 2·8 cm i.d. and the bottom section, 30 cm × 1·4 cm i.d.)
Adsorbent : sample wt. ratio = 18·5 : 1.

Column 4: (Upward elution)   499 g of activated alumina (100—200 mesh, Grade I activation) contained in a glass column. This column consisted of two sections, the lower one measuring 100 cm × 2·4 cm i.d., and the upper, 29 cm × 1·4 cm i.d.
Adsorbent : sample wt. ratio = 12·7 : 1.

Fractionating Columns:

8 plate: 6 cm × 0·6 cm i.d. packed with 1/16-in. Dixon gauze rings.

12 plate: 15 cm × 0·6 cm i.d. packed with 1/16-in. Dixon gauze rings.

DISCUSSION

DR. R. J. MORLEY (*National Coal Board, London*):
I think I ought to start by congratulating Dr. Watson and Mr. Fowler Williams on the large amount of information they managed to extract from such a small sample of tar; it is really amazing

that 2 kilograms of tar should contain so much information! Now, in this country, rather in contrast to most other countries, there is in production well over a million tons a year of vertical-retort tar from gasworks. This tar is quite different from coke-oven tar, being characterized by containing more phenols (particularly higher phenols), very little naphthalene, more paraffins, and is obtained in a higher yield per ton of coal than is coke-oven tar. It seems to me, from the evidence in the report, that the tars examined at Stoke Orchard are rather similar in character to these gasworks vertical-retort tars, and I would like to ask Dr. Watson whether he would comment on the similarity and differences between the gasworks vertical-retort tar and the tar he examined.

The problem of obtaining the maximum value from tar has been before the gas industry for a very long time. Despite this and despite a lot of work done on the subject, the value of vertical-retort tar is still only about 150 shillings per ton; this is about the same value as a fuel oil. Our friends in the coalite business have perhaps managed to do rather better than this with their low-temperature tar, but this is of course on a relatively small scale. In particular, all efforts so far to break down these high-boiling materials (particularly phenols) into lower-boiling materials which are more valuable, have been unsuccessful. I wonder whether Dr. Watson and his colleagues will tell us in what new ways they think they will be able to succeed in obtaining high value for these tars, where the gas industry has failed for so many years.

AUTHOR (MR. A. F. WILLIAMS):

I am glad to have this opportunity of replying to Dr. Morley's questions, because in presenting our paper Dr. Watson and I knew that the theme of most of the questions asked at this Conference would be: " in view of what has been found out, what is proposed should be done with this tar? "

We would agree in general with the conclusion that our tar compares in nature with that of a vertical-retort tar. We say this from a knowledge of the work which is reported in our paper and also from conclusions which we have drawn from later work. But one cannot be too definite about this; if you want to make a fair comparison between two tars, you must make sure that they are examined in exactly the same way. Our examination was of rather a specialized nature and as far as I know, it has not been carried out on the more normal types of tar. However, there is an excellent compilation of data in the Coal-Tar Data Book issued by the Coal Tar Research Association, which covers the normal types of tar. In this book, the following composition is quoted for a vertical-retort tar; pitch content, 40% to 50%, tar acid content of 10% to 15%, a naphthalene content of 3% to 8% and a paraffins content of the order of 5% to 10%. Making such comparisons as I can with the results of our own work, I would say that in terms of pitch content the two types of tar are similar but the tar-acid content of fluid-bed tar is probably higher than that of vertical-retort tars. The naphthalene content, which is not mentioned in our paper, since we determined it only on later samples, is very small indeed—of the order of 0·2% wt. Fluid-bed neutral oil is mainly of the oily, alkylated aromatic type, whereas vertical-retort tars can contain up to about 3% wt. of naphthalene, for example.

There are some similarities and some differences between the two tars. As a general conclusion, I would perhaps agree that fluid-bed tar resembles vertical-retort tar more closely than any other.

Now, what do we propose doing with this tar? It is very high boiling and unless we can do something to change its nature and, in particular, to reduce its boiling range, its usefulness may not be as high as we had hoped. The high-temperature tar industry in general does not investigate the upgrading of its crude tar, as distinct from the refining of it. We would agree that work on thermal cracking is not altogether promising although we are continuing to explore its possibilities on our tar. Hydrogenation is technically feasible, if economically not very attractive on creosote; we have commissioned a small continuous hydrogenation plant and we hope to have our first results within a few months.

DR. D. McNEIL (Coal Tar Research Association, Leeds):

First of all, like Dr. Morley, I wish to pay a tribute to the very elegant technique which the workers who have written this paper used with their tar. I think, of course, this technique was dictated by the thermal instability of the tar, and in fact, it was the inevitable technique to use with this kind of material. But there are two points on which I would like to comment with regard to the technique used. The first point is that I think they are somewhat pessimistic in labelling the material insoluble in benzene/alcohol " entrained coal ". In high-temperature tar, an appreciable amount of material is insoluble in these solvents. This material—or a considerable amount of it—is soluble in more polar solvents and when examined by osmotic-pressure measurements, is found to have a molecular weight of the order of 1000 to 2000; in other words, it is not of particularly high molecular weight and not very much of it is what can possibly be regarded as entrained coal. That particular fraction of the higher-temperature tars is rather an important one, because there is some evidence to show that it is closely associated with the binding power of the pitch. I feel that with this tar, as with more conventional tars, the most obvious use of the residue formed on distillation will be as a binder.

The other point which I would like to comment on refers to the chromatographic separation of the neutral oils. I have privately asked the authors whether this was carried out in an inert atmosphere and their answer is " No ". We did find some time ago when chromatographing high-temperature pitch that there was a considerable amount of oxygen pick-up from the atmosphere on silica or alumina columns. The fractions obtained contained appreciably more oxygen than the material put in. I think this point should be checked as to whether traces of CO groups and hydroxyl groups in the eluate from chromatographic separation are partly due to pick-up of atmospheric oxygen during the separation. The assay method adopted, while ingenious, has I am afraid the disadvantage that, not having been applied to the more normal conventional tars, it is difficult to compare this NCB tar with the more usual tars. At least, I would say it is difficult to compare the NCB tar with the tars whose economic utilization we know at present. Dr. Morley says it appears to be similar to vertical-retort tar. It does in some ways. On the other hand, in its very high phenolic content, particularly its higher content of dihydric phenols, in the almost complete absence of unsubstituted aromatic compounds such as napthalene, and in its wax content it does appear to be similar to a more normal low-temperature tar. On the other hand, it differs from such tars in two points which I think are very significant. First of all, it is a much more viscous material and it appears from the results in the paper we have just heard read that the molecular weight range is rather restricted. There is a very considerable amount of material of about 200 to 400. That of course may be partly due to the fact that, as pointed out in the paper, some of the tar, presumably the most volatile material, was lost by inadequate condensation during carbonization. But the other point, I think, is more important: this tar seems to me quite unique in the fact that it contains a high proportion of substituted benzenes and naphthalenes with long aliphatic side-chains. Now even with vertical-retort tar we find side-chains containing more than two carbon atoms—i.e. ethyl groups—are extremely rare and I would suggest in passing that sulphonation of some of the neutral oil fractions might give materials of considerable importance in the detergent field. I feel, however, that the most valuable component will prove to be the phenols, particularly the dihydric phenols. In this connection, it would appear desirable to recover the phenols in the aqueous liquor by, for example, butyl acetate extraction. This would, I feel, not only be necessary for the recovery of this valuable material for sale, but also help to deal with what might be a very serious effluent problem if large-scale production of such tar becomes an economic possibility. Then again, I would imagine the pitch produced by distillation of this tar would present some interesting possibilities. It will probably be pigmentable and useful as a binder in floor tiles, etc., and as a base for bitumen enamels.

The question has been raised whether it is an economic possibility to crack higher-boiling tar distillates, so as to obtain the more useful lower-boiling components. Well, in the tar acids field, I think everyone who has ever had tar acids to deal with has tried this particular process, and so far the results have been very unpromising, largely because the hydroxyl groups will not survive the conditions required to remove the alkylated side-chains. In the case of the hydrocarbons however the position is much more hopeful. It is possible to break down long-chain alkylated aromatics quite readily to the parent hydrocarbon, and this can be done easily over a nickel catalyst, providing sulphur is first removed; there are several other processes using sulphur-resistant catalysts, which are quite selective to this reaction. In the case of vertical-retort oils, there is a complicating factor in that the high amount of paraffin, which is cracked to carbon and gas, causes the reaction to be extremely exothermic. In the case of the coke-oven material the amount of alkylated aromatics is relatively low and the yield of valuable lower-boiling aromatics in this case is not economically attractive.

That is all I have to say, except for one final point. I am very glad to hear this paper read, because I think the organic chemist has had a very thin time at this conference so far.

MONSIEUR M. DELASSUS (*Charbonnages de France, Noeux-les-Mines*):

I have three questions to put. Dr. Watson used a reactor of 2-inches diameter. Would not the results have been different with one of larger size? The coal was fluidized by steam; would not the tar have been different if inert gas had been used instead of steam? Does not the quality of the tar depend on the velocity of the fluidizing gas?

AUTHOR (MR. A. F. WILLIAMS):

It is very interesting that the questioner should raise the point of the variation or possible variation of the nature of the tar with the diameter of the reactor in which it is produced. In this programme we have to follow on behind our Carbonization Department and examine the tars which they produce. The 2-inch reactor was the first experimental reactor. Later, a 6-inch reactor was adopted and subsequently this was replaced by one of 8-inches diameter. Without quoting experimental evidence, we give it as our impression that the nature of the tar—particularly in respect of boiling range and perhaps also the degree of aromaticity—did in fact change with size of reactor. We have not yet had an opportunity of repeating our first results with the smallest reactor so we cannot be very definite about this.

With regard to the second question, the effect of steam. Our fluid bed carbonizer (8-inch) has latterly been operated with air as the fluidizing gas. The tar which was produced was again slightly different from that made by steam fluidization in the 2-inch reactor. One could predict perhaps that the lower-boiling components of the tar would in fact burn away in air at the temperatures employed (about 600°C), thus rendering the product higher-boiling in nature. The phenol content of the tar appears to have decreased, from the earlier observations of 20% to 30%, to rather less than 20%. I prefer not to go into details on this, because it is the subject of present work in the establishment.

Then the last question, regarding the velocity of the fluidizing gas. I do not think we can answer this. We have examined no samples of tar concerning which we were told that this factor had been altered in the carbonizing conditions.

MR. H. F. BONDY (*Coalite and Chemical Products, Ltd., Chesterfield*):

I have only been able to compare very superficially the tar under discussion with a coalite tar. What strikes me is the enormous difference between a normal low-temperature tar and this tar. The coalite tar is very similar to the tar which is produced by the Carbolux process or by the Lurgi (Velsen) plant, but in this new tar we have something completely different.

With regard to the pitch, you gave the pitch content as 35%. This seems to be not very high because, if this tar were distilled under vacuum, you would probably produce a much lower amount of pitch. On the other hand, the tar is very much higher boiling than a normal low-temperature tar. The question which should be investigated is, what has happened? Has the tar become oxidized during fluidization, has a secondary reaction taken place, or is your tar much more primary in nature than the coalite tar? If the latter is the case, then a suitable breakdown in the retorts by the coalite process takes place, but I do not believe that the matter is so simple and would therefore recommend that this question is further investigated.

INDUSTRIAL TREATMENT OF TAR OBTAINED
BY LOW-TEMPERATURE CARBONIZATION

By J. L. SABATIER

Charbonnages de France, Merlebach, France

Summary—In recent years the Houillères de Bassin de Lorraine have obtained a certain degree of experience in the treatment, on the industrial scale, of tars obtained from low-temperature carbonization. The nature and composition of these tars present new technical and commercial problems.

The treatment comprises a primary fractionation by distillation, secondary treatments of certain fractions—in particular the extraction of the phenols—and finally the preparation of chemical products from the substances obtained from these treatments; examples of the methods used are esterification, hydrogenation and isobutylation.

The distillation plant for the tar employs a 27-plate column, a pipe still, and equipment for preparing the pitch in the form of plates, on a rubber belt.

The dephenolization of the oils is carried out in a continuous process, using soda and sulphuric acid. The crude phenols are fractionated in continuous operation. Discontinuous rectification makes it possible to remove the pure products.

The greatest precautions must be taken to avoid cracking and corrosion.

Certain oils have been found suitable for specific applications of great interest: denapthalization, impregnation, disinfection, and waterproof covering.

Progress in the understanding of the special properties of these tars should open up new prospects for their utilization.

Résumé—Les Houillères du Bassin de Lorraine ont acquis au cours des dernières années une certaine expérience dans le traitement, à l'échelle industrielle, de goudrons obtenus par carbonisation à basse temperature. La nature et la composition de ces goudrons posent des problèmes techniques et commerciaux nouveaux.

Le traitement comporte un fractionnement primaire par distillation, des traitements secondaires sur certaines fractions, en particulier l'extraction des phénols, enfin des fabrications chimiques basées sur les produits obtenus: estérification, hydrogénation, isobutylation par exemple.

La distillation de goudron comprend une colonne de 27 plateaux, un pipe still et un conditionnement du brai en plaquettes sur bande en caoutchouc.

Le déphénolage des huiles se fait en continu à la soude et à l'acide sulfurique. Les phénols bruts sont fractionnes en continu. Une rectification discontinue permet d'extraire les produits purs.

Les plus grandes précautions doivent être prises pour éviter le cracking et les corrosions.

Certaines huiles ont trouvé des applications spécifiques intéressantes: dénaphtalinage, imprégnation, désinfection, revêtements.

Les progrès dans la connaissance des qualités propres de ces goudrons doivent enoore ouvrir des perspectives nouvelles.

Zusammenfassung—Die Houillères du Bassin de Lorraine haben im Laufe der letzten Jahre gewisse Erfahrungen in der Aufbereitung und Verarbeitung von Schwelteeren in technischem Massstab gewonnen. Art und Zusammensetzung dieser Teere bringen neuartige technische und wirtschaftliche Probleme mit sich.

Der Schwelteer wird zunächst durch Destillation in verschiedene Fraktionen zerlegt. Diese werden dann zum Teil weiterbehandelt. Vor allem werden die Phenole abgeschieden. Aus den anfallenden Produkten werden chemische Präparate gewonnen, beispielsweise durch Veresterung, Hydrierung und Isobutylierung.

Die Destillier-Anlage umfasst eine Säule mit 27 Böden, einen Röhrenofen und ein Gummiband, auf dem das Pech in Form von Täfelchen anfällt. Die Entphenolung geschieht kontinuierlich mit Natronlauge und nachfolgender Ausfällung durch Schwefelsäure. Die Rohphenole werden kontinuierlich fraktioniert. Durch diskontinuierliche Rektifizierung kann man Reinerzeugnisse herausschneiden. Grosste Vorsicht ist geboten, um Krackung und Korrosion vorzubeugen. Einige der gewonnen Öle lassen sich mit Vorteil für besondere Zwecke verwenden, z.B. als Naphthalin-waschöl (zur Entnaphthalierung von Kokereigasen), als Imprägnieroder Desinfektionsmittel oder als Anstrich-und Gussmasse.

Eine vertiefte Einsicht in Wesen und Eigenschaften dieser Schwelteere kann weitere, bisher nicht zu übersehende Verwendungsmöglichkeiten erschliessen.

LOW-TEMPERATURE tar, that is to say, tar which is obtained by carbonization of coal carried out at temperatures below 600°C, differs considerably from coke-oven tar, as is well known.

It is distinguished from the latter by its high content of phenolic substances, by the absence of polynuclear hydrocarbons which can be crystallized—such as naphthalene and anthracene—and by the complexity of its chemical composition; a further distinction is that it has a relatively low pitch content.

The special complexity of its chemical constitution is shown both by the diversity of its constituent molecules (which comprise, in particular, an appreciable proportion of aliphatic compounds and naphthenic compounds, in addition to aromatic compounds) and by the degree of substitution in these molecules. These two characteristics clearly demonstrate the destructive and " simplifying " effect of high-temperature cracking to which the coke-oven tar has been subjected in the carbonization chamber. It must be remembered that, for one and the same coal, the yield of " tar " is only about 3% to 3·5% for high-temperature carbonization, while it rises to between 8% and 10% for low-temperature carbonization.

As at present practised, the industrial treatment of low-temperature tar follows the same pattern as the traditional treatment to which coke-oven tar is subjected:

A primary fractionation by means of distillation, with the intention of obtaining the sharpest possible cuts between products.

Suitable secondary treatments are carried out on these cuts. These are either physical treatments such as crystallization or distillation or chemical treatments with acid or basic washes. The purpose of these secondary treatments is to recover the most useful molecules, in the purest state possible, so that they can be supplied to the synthetic chemical industry, who use them as raw materials. Other, simpler secondary treatments—generally consisting of redistillation—are also carried out, with the purpose of selecting or preparing certain fractions, whose properties suit them for clearly defined uses.

Finally, in certain cases, the preparation of simple chemical products can be carried out by means of direct reactions, beginning with mixtures of isomers or of substances with the same chemical function.

Nevertheless, the industrial treatment of low-temperature tar presents its own characteristic difficulties; these are due to the greater thermal sensitivity of the tar and to the corrosive properties of certain fractions.

In addition, the refining of the different products involves technical and commercial problems which are very different from those already known in connection with coke-oven tar; these originate in the differences in nature and properties which exist between the corresponding fractions of the two types of tar, although there is also the influence of the fact that hitherto very small quantities have been put on the open market.

PRIMARY DISTILLATION

The crude tar—containing 2% of water—is distilled at Marienau in a conventional unit, comprising a plate column fed from a pipe still.

The choice of the materials for the columns and for the pipe still raised certain problems in connection with corrosion; these difficulties were solved by the use of stainless steel (18% Ni, 8% Cr, 3% Mo) in the "threatened" elements; these are the parts in contact with liquid fractions at a temperature above 230°C. The maximum temperature on leaving the pipe still is 380°C and the pressure 4 kg. The column contains 27 plates.

The primary distillation yields the following fractions:

Fractions	Distillation interval	Proportions on the basis of anhydrous tar
Light oil	up to 185°C	1%
Phenolic oil I	185° — 230°C	2%
Phenolic oil II	230° — 270°C	8%
Denaphthalization oil	270° — 320°C	5%
Heavy oil	320° — 400°C	32%
Pitch (70 KS)		31%
Losses		1%

This unit operates—on a average—for 300 days in a year; regular interruptions are made for maintenance, involving from 10 to 12 days per quarter. During these interruptions the pipe still is cleaned by controlled combustion of the deposits, using a mixture of air and steam.

The pitch is discharged in the form of plates, 3 mm to 5 mm thick, obtained by spreading out the hot pitch at the end of a rubber conveyor belt, which is sprayed with cold water. This gives a continuous plate of pitch, which breaks up at the end of the belt and is discharged directly into trucks. In this form the pitch has only a slight tendency to agglutinate and is easily handled. The water content does not exceed 1%.

SECONDARY TREATMENTS

In the case of low-temperature tars, the industrial secondary treatments hitherto applied are virtually limited to the recovery of phenols, which occur in particularly large quantities.

Phenolic Oil I

This oil (185°C to 230°C) contains an average of 50% of phenolic substances. The dephenolization is carried out using soda, with subsequent neutralization by means of sulphuric acid. These operations are continuous. Solvent extraction or recovery by means of azeotropic distillation have not given economical results hitherto.

The crude phenol obtained contains from 10% to 13% of moisture, which retains some sodium sulphate in solution, the concentration of which may amount to as much as 70 grams/litre.

This pollution hinders the direct utilization of the crude phenol, which is otherwise possible in certain cases A process for dehydration and purification has been developed, using a controlled treatment with concentrated sulphuric acid; the sulphuric acid subsequently serves to neutralize the solution of sodium phenoxide. This makes it possible to reduce the moisture content of the crude phenol to 3%.

By means of distillation, it is possible to obtain a crude phenol which is dehydrated and from which the substances which easily become polymerized as pitch are removed; this is done by using the first two columns in the continuous fractionation plant described below.

The crude phenol so obtained can be used directly in the manufacture of phenolic resins, the composition being suitably adjusted by means of addition of phenol or a mixture of m- and p-cresols. However, these possibilities of application are still restricted at present, and the greater part of the crude phenol produced is rectified, so as to give the different commercial fractions which are in demand.

The fractionation is carried out in a continuously operating plant, under an absolute pressure of 200 mm of mercury; the installation comprises the following columns:

1 pitch column	— 12 plates
1 dehydration column	— 8 plates
1 phenolic acid column	— 47 plates
1 cresol column	— 47 plates
1 m- and p-cresol column	— 47 plates
1 xylenol column	— 14 plates

The continuous rectification of the crude phenol may be carried out to different programmes according to the objects in view. For example, it is possible to obtain the following fractionation of an anhydrous crude phenol:

11% of phenol; 90% pure
9% of o-cresol; 80% pure
25% of mixed m- and p- cresols (40% to 45% m-cresol content)
50% of xylenols (40% of xylenols, b.p. 205°C—230°C and
                                10% of xylenols, b.p. 230°C—240°C)
5% of pitch.

About one third of the fractions obtained by continuous fractionation are suitable for direct commercial use. The other fractions are retreated batchwise in a column of 60 plates, operating under an absolute pressure of 6mm of mercury. This treatment can yield:

phenol with a melting point of 40°C,
o-cresol with a melting point of 31°C,
mixed m- and p-cresols containing more than 50% of m-cresol,
various xylenol fractions demanded by customers.

For these products, the normal fractionation which has been adopted—bearing in mind present applications—gives the following fractions:

cresylic acid I containing 30% of m-cresol,
cresylic acid II containing 10% to 12% of m-cresol,
cresylic acid III containing 20% of 1 : 3 : 5 - xylenol,
cresylic acid IV (225°C to 240°C).

Phenolic Oil II

This oil contains 40% of various phenolic substances: higher homologues of xylenols, oxyhydrindenes, naphthols, dihydric phenols, etc. It would be possible to envisage a partial brief dephenolization using solvents, and this could be followed, if desired, by selective extraction of the dihydric phenols by means of a water wash.

However, since this oil is a particularly active constituent of the creosote used for wood impregnation, and also a good raw material for disinfectant manufacture, there is, at present, no economic interest in carrying out dephenolization, except in very special instances.

APPLICATIONS AND MARKET POSSIBILITIES—ASSOCIATED PRODUCTS

The products obtained from the primary distillation and the secondary treatments fall, as we have just seen, into three groups:

> the phenolic products representing about 10% of the tar,
> the oils   representing about 60% of the tar,
> the pitch   representing about 30% of the tar.

Phenolic Products

Continuous rectification is capable of giving a number of fractions which are readily marketable, particularly in the phenol plastic industry:

> phenol 90%
> mixed *m*- and *p*-cresols containing 40% to 45% of *m*-cresol.

Discontinuous rectification makes it possible to work up the pure products (phenolic acid; *o*-cresol), concentrated products (mixed *m*- and *p*-cresols with more than 50% of *m*-cresol) and fractions which are standardized for particular uses (cresylic acids).

In addition, it allows us to prepare —at the request of the chemical industry— the following " clear-cut " fractions:

> mixed 1 : 2 : 4- and 1 : 2 : 5-xylenols,
> 1 : 3 : 5-xylenol.

The latter may be prepared in a pure state by crystallization.

We have already seen that phenolic oil II can be more or less completely dephenolized; selective washing with water makes it possible to extract from the bulk of phenols recovered, the dihydric phenols (in particular pyrocatechol and methylresorcinol); the remaining mixture can be used to provide intermediates for either plasticizers or disinfectants, after a purification aimed at eliminating unwanted coloration.

In addition to the conventional manufacturing processes starting with the normal commercial product (phenol; mixed *o*- and *p*-cresols and mixed *m*- and *p*-cresols; 1 : 3 : 5-xylenol), certain derivatives which have an industrial interest can be directly prepared from the xylenol or higher phenol fractions, without it being necessary to resort to previous separation of the components.

1. From the xylenol fraction or a part of this fraction, we can obtain triarylphosphates by means of esterification, using phosphorous oxychloride. The triarylphosphates so obtained compare favourably—from the point of view of

stability and plasticizing power—with the tricresylphosphates which are being used to an ever-increasing extent in the development of polyvinyl resins.

2. Catalytic hydrogenation of the xylenols yields alkylcyclohexanols and alkyl-cyclohexanones; these products are used in the print and varnish industry as heavy solvents. These alcohols may also be used in the preparation of plasticizers.

3. Isobutylation is an effective method of obtaining pure isomers—*m*-cresol, *p*-cresol, the 2 : 4-, 2 : 5-, 3 : 4-, 3 : 5-xylenols. Isobutylation also allows of the preparation of isobutyl derivatives, such as *p*- tert-butylphenol, which is used in the preparation of phenolic resins which are soluble in oil—di-tert-butyl-*p*-cresol which is being used to an ever-increasing degree as an anti-oxygen nontoxic material, and di-tert-butyl-*m*-cresol which is used as a stabilizing agent in fuels and in rubber.

Oils

The low-temperature tar oils have special characteristics which distinguish them from high-temperature tar oils and which make it possible to use them for particular applications.

They have a special mixed chemical nature, since they are at one and the same time paraffinic, aromatic, and naphthenic.

They mix well with petroleum oils.

They do not crystallize at low temperatures.

It is possible to recover from phenolic oil I a *dephenolized oil* which is used as an additive to road tars, and is a good base for insecticides and agricultural disinfectants.

Phenolic oil II is, on the one hand, a constituent of creosote for timber impregnation and, on the other hand, a base for disinfectants which are used in the form of soapy emulsions.

The *denaphthalization oil* selected by precise fractionation has been found to be the best denaphthalizing agent for coke-oven gas ; it is now used very widely in the installations of the Charbonnages de France, the Saar Mines, and in the Gaz de France. This product—which is sold under the trade mark of " Denaphthine "—is marked by a capacity of naphthalene retention which exceeds 5% of the weight of oil used; in addition it can be used at low temperatures, down to minus 5°C.

The *heavy oil* is a constituent of creosote, but the fact that it mixes well with petroleum fuels makes it possible to use it as a priming fuel or as a replacement fuel; it can also be used as an additive to road tars.

Pitch

The pitch from low-temperature tar has physical characteristics which are intermediate between those of coke-oven tar pitch and those of petroleum bitumens. It may be used for briquetting coal fines. It is however more advisable to exploit its special characteristics in sealing: water-proofing or air-tight sealing, etc. In addition, trials in the use of soft pitches (i.e. pitches containing fairly large quantities of oil) for the preparation of coated materials used for road dressing are being carried out. In every case the low-temperature tar pitch is competitive with petroleum bitumens.

CONCLUSION

The profitable use of the products obtained from low-temperature tar must follow a different pattern from that adopted with high-temperature tars. Further progress in the knowledge of the specific characteristics of this tar—and also of the methods of treatment—may open up new possibilities. In this field, the British low-temperature tar industry, which has done pioneer work, is continuing to make valuable contributions.

DISCUSSION

DR. D. MCNEIL (*Coal Tar Research Association, Leeds*):

There are three points in this paper which particularly interest me. The distillation of low-temperature tar in a continuous pipe still is described. I would first of all like to know whether the pipe still at Marienau is entirely convection heated. That is, whether all the heat is derived by passing heated flue gas over the outside of the furnace tubes or whether some of the heat is obtained by direct radiation from the furnace. Secondly, I would be glad to know whether the tar before distillation was treated with any alkali solution. In some pipe stills in this country, processing vertical-retort tar, it has been found that corrosion of metals—including stainless steel—is very rapid unless sufficient caustic soda is added to neutralize the fixed ammonium salts. It may be, of course, that ammonium salts were not present in the tar used at Marienau. That is a point which I would very much like information on. The third point is the composition of the higher-boiling tar acids. I notice that in the paper it is stated that in the phenolic oil oxyhydrindenes are present. Recently we have been doing some work on the composition of the tar acids from vertical-retort tar, boiling in the 230°C to 260°C range, and we find that except for 2-methyl 4-ethyl phenol and 3-methyl 5-ethyl phenol, all the major components are these oxyhydrindenes or their methyl or dimethyl homologues. Some of these materials, such as 7-methyl 5-hydroxy hydrindene and 6-methyl 4-hydroxy hydrindene can be quite readily separated in a fairly pure state. I would like to know whether the Lorraine workers have found that these compounds—these oxyhydrindenes—do represent major components of the tar acids above xylenols. I would particularly like to know whether they have done any work at all on the utilization of these oxyhydrindenes.

MONSIEUR J. DERUELLE (*Charbonnages de France, St. Avold*) (*for the author*):

The pipe still at Marienau is convection heated, but we have taken the precaution of providing a system of recycling the hot gases. I am of the opinion that this may not be the best way; in new plants we intend to provide two pipe stills. The plants are intended to treat separately high-temperature and low-temperature tars. The first pipe still, working at a relatively low temperature, will be heated by convection. This gives what is called a soft pitch, i.e. a pitch with a good admixture of oils. The second pipe still heated by radiation deals with this soft pitch and is intended to separate out the pitch.

With regard to the second question: we add sodium carbonate to the tar before distillation. In fact, it is a general precaution in France to add sodium carbonate to the tar but nobody has been able to show that this is very necessary. It is a good precaution, and nobody can take the risk to stop the addition. In fact, at low temperatures we have noticed that we have fixed salts in liquor in the tar. For this, caustic soda may be a good precaution. It is not very expensive.

In reply to the third question, I would say that we have begun the study of the higher phenols, but have not yet obtained results which I would consider worth quoting. It is a very complex study to undertake and as we are business men and not laboratory research workers, we wonder whether it is worth-while going to the extent of starting a long and laborious programme of analysis. Furthermore, we examined the market possibilities, and, in France at least, the position at the present moment is that the market will be very restricted for products of this kind. It is naturally a very long and difficult programme of research, to determine the exact composition, and it may not necessarily be worth-while.

DR. J. SZUBA (*Faculty of Chemistry of Coal Utilization, Polytechnic School, Gliwice, Poland*):

Why—in outlining the distillation of low-temperature tars—were the same temperature ranges used to recover the oil fractions, as are used for high-temperature tar treatment? Such a procedure seems to me to be right for phenolic oil No. 1. For other fractions it is rather questionable, and I would like to know why the author chose this solution.

Gaseous CO_2 has most commonly been used for neutralizing the phenolates. Why was sulphuric acid subsequently used? I would like to know whether this treatment was dictated by the particular course of the reaction or not.

In closing, I would like to say a few words concerning the physicochemical properties of low-temperature tars. I wish to draw your attention to this subject, because the researches of Professor Swietoslawski—a member of the Polish Academy of Sciences—have led us to consider these tars as multicomponent mixtures, whose physical-chemical properties are better known now.

According to his work, the low-temperature tars are formed as complicated mixtures of poly-azeotropes and polyzeotropes. Such a mixture does not contain any particular predominating component, to be obtained by distillation or crystallization. In the composition of the tars, we did not find any particular compound present in such quantities as would justify our considering it as the main " component " of distillation or crystallization. In the case of high-temperature tars, we do always find a predominant " component " of distillation or crystallization and this is the reason for the different behaviour of these tars.

The above-mentioned considerations have led me to put the question, whether it is correct to use the same temperature ranges for recovery of the oil fractions for both kinds of tar.

MONSIEUR J. DERUELLE (*Charbonnages de France, St. Avold*) (*for the author*):

The first question put by Dr. Szuba was why are the same intervals of distillation chosen as for high-temperature tars. I would reply that, if they are in fact identical—or at least similar—it is rather more of a coincidence than anything else. Concerning the Phenolic Oil No. 1 the cut is determined by the xylenol quantity required. You can work at 210°C to 220°C or 230°C, and the content varies according to the temperature chosen. In other words we can do pretty well what we like. With regard to denaphtalization oil which is a very useful product and which fetches a relatively high price, this requires a very clean cut. This is the factor which governs the interval of distillation chosen. With regard to question 2, which asked why sulphuric acid was chosen for neutralization rather than carbon dioxide, in our opinion, the two processes are equally good. There probably will be a renewed discussion on this subject whenever a new plant is to be put up. We thought that the use of carbon dioxide was not advisable, because it requires large capital outlay and a very large plant. There is also an appreciable loss of phenols which are carried along in the gas and thrown out in the discharge. On the other hand, we have a sulphuric acid plant associated with us; this is a good reason for using it. In addition, the plant is smaller and cheaper and no losses of phenols to the atmosphere occur. There are, however, some losses to the residual water from the process. In fact, we have concluded that while the two processes are probably almost on an equal footing economically, the sulphuric acid gave us a simpler and cheaper plant, and we therefore decided to use that.

MR. A. F. WILLIAMS (*National Coal Board, Stoke Orchard*):

The questions which I wish to put to Monsieur Deruelle have occurred to me in looking forward from the more academic investigations, which Dr. Watson and I described this morning, to the commercial difficulties which obviously may arise in transferring such investigations to the commercial scale.

The first point is that all the valuable chemical products appear to arise from Phenolic Oil No. 1. These products are the phenols which are said to be washed out of the oil by caustic soda. No mention is made of any contamination of these phenols with sulphur bodies, bases or neutral oil compounds, which can also occur in the caustic soda by some such process as entrainment or emulsification or solubilization. Have any difficulties been encountered in the purification of phenols liberated from the caustic soda? If so, could Monsieur Deruelle tell us what steps were taken to overcome them?

The second point is one in which we are particularly interested in this country: are there any standard specifications to which the marketable phenols have to conform? I am thinking particularly of such features as: colour, sulphur content, smell, stability to light and air, contents of water, bases, and neutral oils; in addition, do the products which Monsieur Sabatier has described require to be treated in any special way so as to produce these grades? The third point concerns the economics of the processing methods described. To what extent do the phenols have to pay for the refining costs? Shall I put it rather in this way: from which of the main products which have been named— the light oil, or the phenols, or the creosote, or the " denaphthalization oil " (I take it that this is our " benzene-absorbing oil ") or pitch—does the bulk of the revenue derive?

Lastly—and this is a theme which connects with our own paper—none of the neutral oil products described in Monsieur Sabatier's paper finds particularly new application. To what extent does Monsieur Deruelle feel that work on the fundamental structure of these oils is needed; to what extent would such knowledge assist in the better utilization of these oils?

I

MONSIEUR J. DERUELLE (*Charbonnages de France, St. Avold*) (*for the author*):

First question: Did we have difficulties about the purity of the products and emulsification, etc.? We had no difficulty on the dephenolization plant, which worked perfectly well. The plant was built by Koppers of Germany. In fact, the tar oils are eliminated in the phenate by steam entrainment. There is equipment for washing the oil with dilute sulphuric acid to remove the bases. Because the present market is very bad, we do not do so at the moment. I cannot give exact figures for the purity of phenol, but the content of bases must be under 0·1%.

Second question: What about purity, colour, odour and so on of the phenols? At present, there is no standard in France for colour, sulphur content, odour or light stability of the phenols. Much progress should be made, however, in this matter. Certainly, the chemical industry would be glad to have a colourless product. We have now begun a programme on this subject, but cannot yet give complete results. It seems that there are several means of improving the quality of all the characteristics. It is known, for instance, that air blowing gives very interesting results.

With regard to the third question: What are the costs of the process? Mr. A. F. Williams asked if it is possible to make money with low-temperature tars. This is a very important question, to which we attach the greatest importance, since we are business men rather than research workers.

In fact, it depends on the economic conditions in each country:

a) Policy of protecting national products, for motor cars, etc. Light oils and dephenolized oils give good products for cars and diesel motors. But the price will not be sufficient if these products must pay all the taxes generally paid by petrol.

b) Price of the petroleum products for combustion. It is always possible to sell the tar oils for combustion at the same price as the corresponding petroleum products. It is the minimum price.

c) Price of coke-oven tar and of its pitch. These are very different in different countries.

d) Price of the low-temperature tar. There is a very important question in connection with the price of low-temperature tar: Is it possible to expect the low-temperature tar to reach a sufficient value to assure the economic success of the low-temperature carbonization itself? I think it is necessary to be prudent, that is, to book the low-temperature tar at the same price as coke-oven tar. I have been told that many people think that it is possible to earn a good deal of money with low-temperature tar, but I believe that now—especially in America—they think that this is not so certain. Now in America, they say that the price of low-temperature tar must be set at about 20% below coke-oven tar. I think it is possible to do better and to quote the same price, but I think that it is not prudent to expect a better price. In the present conditions in France, we can say that the tar distillation itself—without treatment of the phenol oil—pays its costs. If we count the price of the tar as 1, the price of the products are: pitch, 1·3; heavy fuel oil, 1·2; light fuel oil, 1·5; denaphthalization product, 2; optical low-temperature pitch, 1·5. So it is possible to pay the cost of the distillation of tar by itself, without quoting a very high price for phenolic oil. If we now consider the total revenue, including phenol treatment, we can say that 14% of revenue is obtained from the light oils, 40% from the phenols, 6% from the denaphthalization product, 18% from the heavy oil and 22% from the pitch. So it seems that the phenol, with 40%, is a major contributor to this, but it must be said that the cost involved by the treatment of the phenolic oil and of the crude phenols is very heavy too. In conclusion, I would point out that it is difficult to ensure the economic success of low-temperature carbonization and low-temperature tar treatment, if the capacity of the plants is not sufficient. I think that the minimum capacity for a carbonizing plant is 500 tons per day. A plant over 1000 tons per day will be quite sure to make money. For a tar plant the minimum capacity would be 200 tons per day, which is difficult to obtain with low-temperature tar only, so that it is of great interest to combine the treatment of the low-temperature tar with that of coke-oven tar. The third question, whether it is interesting to engage in research on the neutral oils? I agree with Mr. Williams on the interest of fundamental research on low-temperature oil. I think this is a very long and important task, such as Mr. Williams told us of this morning. The work would better be done by research insitutes than by plant laboratories. We have not the means to undertake such an important study. A probable difficulty in " scaling up " laboratory results to the industrial stage would result from the complexity of this oil, which contains numerous components in equal proportions.

MR. B. ROBSON (*National Coal Board, Stoke Orchard*):

My question has largely been answered by the discussion that has gone before. However, I should like to hear Monsieur Deruelle's views on the selection and operation of large-scale equipment for the processing of low-temperature tars. Do such tars present any novel problems or difficulties which the plant designer is not likely to encounter with high-temperature tars?

MONSIEUR J. DERUELLE (*Charbonnages de France, St. Avold*) (*for the author*):

The distillation of low-temperature tar presents certain special difficulties. For instance, it is normal for a pipe-still tube in ordinary steel to work for two years without difficulty in a coke-oven tar plant. I can say from experience that it would be destroyed by corrosion in a week with low-temperature tar. We concluded that the solution was the extensive use of stainless steel in all parts of the plant which came into contact with tar or oils at temperatures of 200°C or over. Actually, the cost of stainless steel is not so high as is generally thought. The physical properties allow of making a reduction in the thickness of the parts, and the decrease in the total weight obtained—for instance, in comparison with cast iron—gives an appreciable economy in foundations. For instance, in a study for a new plant, it was found that the price for a low-temperature tar plant was only 4% higher than that for a coke-oven tar plant. Another point is the thermal sensitivity of the tar, which by itself has a tendency to crack. This difficulty is increased by the fact that is is necessary to heat this tar in the pipe still at a higher temperature than when treating coke-oven tar, in order to furnish the heat necessary for vaporizing a larger proportion of oil. This is the reason why it may be interesting to choose processes in which the light parts of the tar are maintained at as low a temperature as possible, or in which they do not pass through the pipe still. It is the vaporization of the oil in the pipe still which is dangerous. Nevertheless, we run an ordinary pipe still at 380°C without difficulty. It is simply necessary to clean the pipe still every quarter; naturally, the temperature and pressure have to be very carefully checked and controlled. Another point is the variability of the tar; the conditions of carbonization in coke-ovens are now well established and the tar produced is regular and similar. It is not the same with low-temperature carbonization. The tar produced by different types of oven are quite different. Any change in the carbonization conditions have an influence on the yield and quality of the tar. It is necessary for the carbonization plant to operate very regularly or the operation of the tar plant is very difficult.

CLOSING ADDRESS

By J. Bronowski

Director, Coal Research Establishment, National Coal Board

THE words chemical engineering in the title of this conference were a bold and ambitious choice. We thought it important to underline what we believe to be the coming importance of the processes of chemical engineering at this, the first conference held here. Chemical engineering is not new in the coal industry, but we think that the part it has to play in the future will be many times larger than that which it plays now, and we believe therefore that the chemical treatment of different coals must be made a more and more exact science.

Much of what we have talked about in the last two days has been the subject of discourse in the oil industry for many years—some of it for fifty years. Yet there is no scientific reason why research on coal should lag behind research on oil. There is no reason why coal should continue to be treated as the poor relation among the fossil fuels. All of us at this conference, we from this establishment and our colleagues from many other countries who are here today, are united by the hope that we are moving into a period in which there will be applied to coal the same detailed and exact study which has made the oil industry great.

All over the world there has been in the last ten years a renaissance in the application of science to traditional industries—industries which in the past have not been thought important enough, or have not yielded a large enough profit, to make their scientific study worth while. Since coal costs only about a penny a pound to the consumer, it is of course more difficult to introduce chemical engineering into its preparation than into, say, the preparation of copper. But we live in an age in which scarcity has become as important as money value. Coal is cheap, but it is now fairly scarce; and that, I think, is the real context of the work we have been doing and describing in the last two days.

No conference on this scale would have been possible twenty-five years ago. This was not for lack of pioneers in the application of science to coal. There were pioneers twenty-five years ago; important research work was done then; great names and reputations were established. But there simply did not exist at that time scientific talent in industry on the scale that is assembled in this room and backed up in your laboratories. Today, we have enough scientists to be aware that we need more; we have the will to use them in the traditional industries; and we have behind them the technological skill which can translate the blackboard diagrams of the last two days into practical processes.

There are many nations in this room, and the problems of each nation are a little different. The French contributions to the conference have centred on the problem of producing good coke from coals which do not, in the first place, lend themselves to coking. The same problem, the shortage of good coking coals, was seen even more acutely in the contribution from Poland. One contribution from Germany laid special emphasis on a subject which no-one else discussed, namely the making of briquettes for the special purpose of smelting. In America, as you know, the major interest of research into coal is to turn it into liquid products.

We in this establishment concentrate our work on one problem above others: the making of efficient fuels for the open fire. This is a peculiar problem, which has been created for us by the use in Great Britain of those curious and (you may think) prehistoric grates, two of which you have seen burning as a constant reminder in the entrance halls to the conference. Whatever you may think of these grates, about fourteen million houses in this country have them; and so long as these houses stand, over thirty million tons of coal a year must be burnt in them. For this reason, our research here is dominated by the problem of developing fuels which are efficient when burnt in the open grate. This of course is the same as the problem of developing fuels which are smokeless when burnt in the open grate. It was nobody in this establishment or at this conference who first said that the thing to do with the smoke in the coal is to burn it: that was said by Benjamin Franklin almost two hundred years ago.

Today we are no longer content to get rid of the smoke merely by burning it; as this conference has shown, we want to turn it into byproducts. But the thought remains the same: that to let the smoke go up the chimney is not only noxious, it is hopelessly wasteful. This is why research in this establishment concentrated on smokeless house fuels long before smokelessness became a public crime; because they are efficient fuels.

There is throughout Europe (and indeed the world) today a growing need for energy. All the nations are starved for energy. They can get more energy in three ways. They can step up the output from existing sources; that is, they can dig more coal and drill for more oil. They can bring in new sources of energy: atomic energy, the wind, the sun. And they can use the existing sources more efficiently, to get more energy out of a ton of coal or oil than they do now.

Throughout western Europe, the average efficiency at which coal is used is still less than 25%. Of every four miners who work and sometimes die underground, three do so to no purpose. Only one of them digs coal which is really used; the other three might as well take the coal that they dig and shovel it straight up the chimney. Therefore an important reservoir of energy, and in Great Britain the most important reservoir we have at hand, is the energy we waste.

The processes on which we are working in this establishment are designed to use this reservoir; and this desire has been a common thread running through the contributions to this conference. We are all trying to make of coal, the natural fuel, a better fuel which shall no longer be largely wasted in the burning. We are all aware that we shall continue to depend on coal as the basic source of energy for some decades. You have sensed this in the contributions from the nations in this room, and it is as true of the nations not here. Your president in his opening address yesterday drew attention to the fact that the representatives of the National Coal Board who have just toured Russia found that coal is and will continue to be basic in her economy.

There is sometimes talk which implies that the coming of atomic energy will at once make the winning of coal useless. So pessimists used to say, on three days in the week, that the coming of oil would make the winning of coal useless. (On the other three days, of course, they said that the oil was going to run out in a few years anyway.) But the fact is that we live, and shall live for at least thirty years, in an age in which every source of energy is needed to sustain the continued industrial expansion and the prosperity of all countries. We do not live in a time when there is competition between fuels; we live in a time when there is a famine for energy.

These general remarks are designed to put this conference into the perspective of world needs on the one hand, and of our work in this establishment on the other. In this setting, I should like now to summarize the discussions which have been held during these two days.

M. Boyer and Dr. Jenkins both read papers on the oxidation of coal. In the main, both were oxidizing for the same purpose: namely, to reduce the swelling and sticking of the coal. But the discussions went further, and enumerated in a very interesting way the many effects which oxidation has on coal. For example, Dr. Huck drew attention to the importance in everyday processes of the natural oxidation which takes place when you simply store coal. He made a second remark, which I have thought about several times in the discussion of tars today; he remarked how profound is the effect of the oxidation of coal on the byproducts which are made from it. When coal is processed in any low- or medium-temperature plant or fluidizer, the yield and nature of the byproducts are changed (and usually changed for the worse) if the coal has been oxidized—whether it has been oxidized intentionally or unintentionally.

Equally the oxidation of coal affects the coke that is made from it. Mr. Kennaway showed that oxidized coals usually give more reactive cokes. There was a difference of opinion on the mechanism which brought about this and other changes. Dr. Gillings and Mr. Lawson held that the main effect of oxidation is to change the plasticity or fluidity of the coal while it is turning into coke. M. Boyer thought this less important than another effect of oxidation, which is that at the same time it changes the shrinkage characteristics.

These and other uncertainties all stem back to our ignorance of fundamentals in the oxidation of coal. As Dr. Standing pointed out, we know very little of the underlying mechanism by which coal is oxidized. This is a field in which, as he implied, nothing is certain except our ignorance.

For instance, Mr. Bond, M. Boyer and Dr. Ingram discussed, as a possible model of the process of oxidation, the hypothesis that the added oxygen attaches itself to free radicals, and they came to conflicting conclusions.

I should like to suggest that we should not be wholly preoccupied, as we were in this theoretical discussion, with the noncrystalline constituent of coal, in which the free radicals are to be found. In my view, one result of oxidation is, as it were, to stiffen the crystalline framework which is provided by the layers of graphite in the coal. Oxides of graphite are of two kinds and behave in two ways; in one, the oxygen is sandwiched between the layers of graphite, and in the other it bonds or clips the layers together. I think that we shall understand the fundamentals of the oxidation of coal better when we have studied its effect in stiffening the graphite skeleton.

There are chemical additives other than oxygen which reduce the swelling and sticking of some coals. I was therefore interested to find in the discussion references to the action of these additives, from which something might be learnt about their mechanism. In particular, of course, additives are already used to improve coke and coke briquettes. Alas, although many laboratories must be doing research on them, none understands their mode of action any better than that of oxygen.

The fluid bed for the oxidation of coal which Dr. Jenkins described is a pilot plant with a throughput of a ton an hour, and I hope that you will all take the opportunity to see it running before you leave. In the discussion on it, comparisons were made between its operation and that of other forms of oxidizer, and the question was inevitably asked whether any plant which pretreats coal could be made to pay. It seems to me that this question is a ghost from an earlier time. Today a coke oven or other coking plant with its ancillaries costs so much that the cost of subsidiary treatments is trifling by comparison. There is no oxidation process whose cost— capital cost and running cost—is more than a small fraction of the ordinary cost today of building a large plant, handling the material in and the product out, and all the other basic costs of treating coal by any of the traditional processes.

I should like to underline this point in order firmly to fix a fallacy which is still prevalent in the coal industry, and which the oil industry and the atomic energy industry have got rid of. The fallacy is that it costs markedly more to run a two-stage or a three-stage process than it costs to run a single-stage process. It is the mark of the primitive industries that they are addicted to single-stage processes. In the advanced industries it has been realized that once a plant is put up at all to process the raw material, the bulk of the cost is already committed. The number of steps in the process is relatively a small item of cost to be added to the absolute and basic cost of putting the raw material into the plant, handling it through the plant, and getting it out again.

The economic cost of processing a material must be measured by one criterion only: what is the value of the added efficiency with which the processed material can be used? For example, President Eisenhower announced not long ago that America was willing to sell enriched uranium to other nations, and he quoted a price. The price, very roughly, was a million pence a pound—that is, about a million times the price of coal. Since the fission of a pound of uranium yields a million times as much energy as the burning of a pound of coal, this is a very reasonable price. It is not over-weighted either by the cost of digging the ore, or by the number of stages through which it has been taken. In the same way, the oil industry measures price by efficiency of use and is not afraid of multistage processes. The lesson will be important for the coal industry in the future.

In describing our pilot plant for oxidation in a fluid bed, Dr. Jenkins made a remark which seemed to me to have much theoretical interest. He said that it had been impossible to calculate accurately the heat of the reaction until the work had reached the scale of a ton an hour. There I think he touched on a difficulty in working with a nonhomogeneous material such as coal which is not always grasped by the laboratory worker. The laboratory worker is used to having a homogeneous material, and he therefore supposes that one experiment, if done accurately enough, should give him a value which he will find in every experiment. When he works with coal, however, this is no longer true; he must take a thousand samples even from a single seam, and average the result of a thousand experiments. The fluid bed is an industrial apparatus, but it has this advantage as an experimental apparatus, that of itself it averages many thousand values without ever using a calculating machine. In this establishment, we have taken advantage of this property of the fluid bed in other calculations—for example, in the calculation of the heat of carbonization which Mr. Owen presented.

The afternoon session yesterday was concerned with briquetting. I was particularly interested in that part of Dr. Reerink's paper which described the making of briquettes to replace furnace and foundry coke. I believe that important developments in metallurgy, and particularly in the foundry, will follow when coke as it is now made is replaced by coked briquettes which are uniform in size, density and strength.

In the discussion on Dr. Reerink's paper, Dr. Baum described one method to speed up the process of carbonization. This is the slowest and therefore the costliest step in the processing of coal, and there was evidently a wide interest in the conference in devices which would cut the time and with it the cost of carbonization. Let me therefore invite you, when you look over the establishment, to visit an experimental plant which we did not describe to the conference. It is a carbonizer in which the heat is transferred to briquettes by a solid, namely by hot sand, instead of as at present by a gas.

Dr. Reerink spoke of a special binder, Teerpechschmelze, which is coming into use in the making of dense briquettes, and the discussion suggested that this binder was akin to a cutback pitch. A variety of such liquid binders with special properties is now entering the briquetting industry, and is replacing the traditional binders such as pitch. In this, as in other matters, the different countries represented at this conference are working with very similar ideas. Indeed, in this discussion, Dr. Kardaun produced an idea from Holland which both gratified and dismayed me; for we have been nursing it for some time in this establishment, confident that it was so good an idea that nobody else would be able to make it work in practice. The idea is one for making a smokeless fuel in the form of briquettes which do not need to be carbonized. To do this, one must of course start with a smokeless coal or coke powder; and what is more difficult, one must compact it with a binder which is itself effectively smokeless. Dr. Kardaun revived a proposal which has been made before, but which has never been made to work: to use another coal as the binder, and to use it hot. This is close to some of the work which Mr. Gregory described, in which hot coal is used as a binder and is, for this purpose, made to flow by being mixed with pitch.

I found Mr. Gregory's paper difficult to follow because it seemed to me to combine two topics which are really separate; and it may therefore be helpful if I take them apart. In both parts of his paper, Mr. Gregory was concerned with briquetting at a high temperature; but he was concerned with it in the two parts for different reasons and, essentially, by different methods. In the first part, he simply wanted to save heat from going to waste. If coal has to be pretreated, then briquetted, and then carbonized, then (he argued) it is a pity to have the briquetting temperature lower than the temperatures of pretreatment and of carbonization. He therefore set himself to develop a method by which coal could be briquetted when hot, and he found such a method and found that it saved a good deal of the pitch which is used in briquetting. This summarizes the first part of Mr. Gregory's paper.

But at the temperatures at which he was now briquetting, 300°C and more, Mr. Gregory was faced by a puzzle. At these temperatures, the pitch flows freely and does not bind the coal. What does it do instead? Mr. Gregory found that it acts as a flux, and widens the range of temperature in which the coal is plastic and is itself capable of binding. This led him to the thought that hot coal and pitch can be mixed together to make a compound binder, which can then be used to bind an already smokeless coal or coke powder into briquettes.

This thought Mr. Gregory has worked out in the second part of his paper. Here the likeness to what Dr. Kardaun proposed in the discussion is plain. Where Dr. Kardaun has it in mind to use a smokeless coal powder, as the main content of the briquette, Mr. Gregory may use coke breeze or char. And where Dr. Kardaun has it in mind to use a high-volatile coal, as the binder for the briquette, Mr. Gregory will use a compound binder of coal fluxed with pitch.

It was in a later discussion that Mr. Szpilewicz described a multistage process of carbonization, briquetting and further carbonization which may have to be used in Poland in order to make a strong metallurgical coke. I draw attention to it here, however, because the methods of briquetting which have been described may be relevant to it; and because, like the work which Dr. Reerink presented, it shows that briquetting may become a necessary step in the making of strong cokes.

I pass now to our sessions of today. This morning M. Foch read, on his behalf and on that of M. Peytavy, a paper on partial carbonization in a fluid bed. This paper aroused, I think, wider interest than any other, and because it was so widely and well discussed, I need not analyse it in the detail which I have given for Mr. Gregory's paper. One incidental piece of information which struck me from the outset was that the bed had usually been worked either at 500°C or at 800°C. It has also been our experience in this establishment that these are good temperatures to carbonize coal in a fluid bed, and that by contrast it is unwise to work between these two temperatures. As Mr. Owen showed in the discussion, if one carbonizes some high-volatile coals between these temperatures, one may have to supply more than twice as much heat to the process as one would need at 500°C, or perhaps at 800°C.

This strange finding shows how important it is in all the work to which this conference is devoted to base the practical development on strict scientific findings. Nothing is easier than to build a plant of this kind and decide to run it at 650°C because the pilot plant has run well at 500°C and at 800°C. But the sequence of reactions which we exploit in carbonization is not collectively linear; and in assuming light-heartedly that it is, we may multiply our plant and running costs several times.

If these cautions seem to show a bias towards scientific theory, let me correct this at once by applauding a very practical remark which M. Foch made. He said that the size of a plant which uses fluid beds may be limited, in the last analysis, by the harrassing difficulty of getting the dust out of the gases. Dr. Morley also pointed to this difficulty, and we must conclude that it constitutes the outstanding problem in all the processes we have discussed which use fluidization to treat or to handle powdered coal.

The problem of recovering dust is a mechanical one; it is matched by the chemical problem of recovering the byproducts in their best form. As Mr. Greenwood pointed out, to get all the byproducts and to use them well is essential to the economics of every process of carbonization, even the traditional carbonization in the coke oven. This was in fact the theme of the paper by M. Sabatier which was read for him this afternoon by M. Deruelle. M. Sabatier's paper, and the earlier paper by Dr. Watson and Mr. Williams, showed in detail that the tars which are produced in low-temperature carbonization and in the fluid bed have their own special natures. The tars that Dr. Watson and Mr. Williams described contain a disproportionate amount of high-boiling phenols and of high-boiling neutral oils. Dr. Morley pointed out that they therefore have some likeness to the tars made when coal is carbonized in vertical retorts, and Dr. Bondy pointed out that they are unlike the tar made when coal is carbonized to make Coalite. As Dr. McNeil remarked, it may be that the tar made when coal is partially carbonized in a fluid bed is easily oxidized; if this is so, it has the same disadvantages as tar made from an oxidized coal, at which I have already glanced.

M. Sabatier's paper was most ingenious in taking a medium temperature tar to pieces in such a way that the fractions could all be sold in some market already created by conventional high temperature tar. Yet I am sure that what Dr. McNeil said on this topic is right: the new tars cannot be used to the best advantage in the conventional pattern of the existing market for byproducts. New markets must be created for the new tars; new products must be evolved which use effectively the special constituents of these tars. Only so can the true value of the byproducts from new processes be recovered. And if the users will not give thought to the special value and uses of these new byproducts, then the coal industry will have to do so.

Having thus reviewed the papers and the discussions of the conference, let me now draw some general conclusions from them. They revealed several unsolved problems, to which I have referred, and which I ought to underline. One is the difficulty of removing the entrained solids from the gas stream after any process of fluidization. In the sort of plant that we have in mind, with a throughput of a thousand tons a day, it would be very unpleasant to the neighbourhood to have 1% or 2% of the product blow through the cyclones into the air; and more than unpleasant, it might be catastrophic to the economics of the process. The fluidized treatment and fluidized handling of coal is, however, the most direct way of handling the solid in a continuous manner. Therefore the prospect of introducing the continuous processes of modern chemical engineering into the coal industry may depend critically on our ability to keep the powder of the fluid bed in the plant.

I have just referred to the second practical conclusion: the importance of creating special uses for the special byproducts which the new processes will yield. We can go on for a time selling them in existing markets, and making them into the same ashtrays, fibres and antiseptics which are made from the constituents of high temperature tars. But if new processes (for example, carbonization in a fluid bed) are to reach an output measured at least in hundreds of thousands of tons a year, then a large effort in chemical research and development will be required which looks at the byproducts afresh, in their own right, as new raw materials for new applications. We can then no longer be content, as we were in this conference, merely to ask " Who wants this byproduct now? " We shall have to ask ourselves, and challenge new users to ask, " What can this byproduct be made to do ?"

The discussions showed how great remains the need for a scientific understanding of the fundamental transformations of coal: in particular, of oxidation, and of the sequence of changes which is called carbonization. A great deal of what is called science in the traditional industries still consists of the framing of mere verbal explanations which do no more than paraphrase the familiar phenomena. Nowadays these explanations are couched in a more learned jargon than they were in the past, when it was sufficient to say that " coal has an affinity for oil " and " shale has no affinity for oil ". But a more impressive jargon does nothing to make explanations of this kind more penetrating. Too many explanations in the traditional industries still do not conform to the true requirements of science; they do not give an insight into what is happening, and they do not give us the foresight to change what is happening. What is needed to prepare firm foundations for new processes (and, for that matter, to improve old processes) is research designed to elucidate the underlying physical and chemical mechanisms which cause the known changes in coal.

The conference has shown that fundamental research of this kind is going on; that in all countries, great advances have been made in it in the last years; and that the body of scientific knowledge on coal is growing impressively. I think that the conference showed too that the advances of recent years are ahead of their application, and that the treatment of coal could be revolutionized by putting into practice now the scientific findings which are well founded and known. In this respect, the lesson of the conference is surely that research has reached very similar results in all countries, but that development is very unequal in different countries.

In this country, in this establishment, we are most often still at the stage of developing new work on the scale of a ton a day. In France, as the conference has heard, more developments have reached the scale of a ton an hour. The ambitious pilot plant which Dr. Reerink sketched is an example of German development on a still larger scale. And the German scale in turn is dwarfed by the known scale of pilot development in America. These differences in the pace of development may well be critical, and may decide which countries will succeed and which will fail to solve their energy crisis in time.

The new processes can help to solve the energy crisis which faces us all. But in the long run, of course, they have a greater importance. In twenty or thirty years' time, by 1975 or 1985, coal used crudely to generate industrial energy will be a poor competitor with atomic energy. The time will then have passed when any form of energy will command a market merely because there is a shortage. It may then no longer be worth while to mine coal in order simply to burn it under boilers, just as today it is no longer worth while to cut down timber in order to burn it. The future of coal on that day, thirty years hence, depends on the direction which we take now. If we exploit the present shortage of energy, and are content to go on selling it as it is to those who must buy it while there is nothing else, then coal will become (when there is something else) not only a fossil fuel but a fossil habit.

The future of coal, the long future, rests on its chemical content. And the far-reaching importance of the new processes which this conference has discussed is, that they are steps towards the future exploitation of this chemical content. We have much to learn here from the oil industry. During the hundred years since oil was first used, and in which it has grown to be a world power, the man who made most money out of it was John D. Rockefeller. Yet when Rockefeller retired, the motor car was still a toy; there was no market for petrol, no-one thought about chemical byproducts, and processes such as catalytic cracking were half a century away. Rockefeller had made none of his money from using oil as we use it. He had made it, every cent of it, by burning the oil in kerosene lamps. The coal industry too can still make money by burning coal under boilers. But it is time that it learnt from the oil industry that it cannot do this for ever, and that there are better things that it can do.

I cannot resist, before I formally close the conference, straying for one informal moment to its origin. The origins of this conference do not grow entirely in coal; they include a little local patriotism. Exactly one hundred years ago, in the year 1856, the British Association for the Advancement of Science met in Cheltenham for the only time in its history. At that meeting, Henry Bessemer read the paper in which he disclosed his new process for making steel. The records of the British Association do not print the paper, nor do they report what was said at the meeting by one of the few engineers who appreciated its importance at once, James Nasmyth. And of course, they contain no echo of the grand and spacious exchanges which followed after the meeting, in which Bessemer offered Nasmyth a third share in the patent (because Nasmyth held some related patents which he waived) and Nasmyth declined it because he had enough money.

The British Association this year is celebrating Bessemer's discovery by meeting, not at Cheltenham, but at Sheffield. But we, in this establishment for industrial research, felt that so great a practical discovery, announced here a hundred years ago by a scientist at a scientific meeting, should not pass without our tribute. This conference may therefore be counted in part as our tribute. And if a conference ought to have a moral, it can be taken from James Nasmyth's account of that meeting. In his autobiography, Nasmyth recalls that at breakfast on the day when Bessemer was to read his paper, he heard an ironmaster scoff at the discovery in Bessemer's hearing. " Did you ever hear of such nonsense?" said the ironmaster; and he was saying no more than practical men often say about new scientific processes. But what Bessemer said was not nonsense; and it is pleasant to record that it was turned into sound sense in the same year, 1856, by a man with a gift for development, Robert Mushet of Coleford in the Forest of Dean, twenty-five miles from here.

And now I have only one final task—a very pleasant one for me. On behalf of the National Coal Board, I have to thank all of you for helping us in this establishment to learn as much as we have done in this conference.

I want to thank those devoted and hard-working people who have written the papers for the conference, those who have contributed to the discussion, the Chairmen who have guided the discussion and the translators who have made us forget that we do not all speak the same language. But above all, I want to thank our visitors from overseas and from the universities whose quiet interest is the real backbone of a conference of this kind.

In my invitation to you to attend this conference I said that the development of modern methods of chemical engineering in the coal industry was a subject of great and growing importance. That, I think, the very practical discussions in this conference have now shown.

And I said that I believed that a conference like this, of scientists and practical men, of those engaged in fundamental work, in development and in the hard needs of industrial application, would help us all to learn from one another. I hope that you feel, as we feel in this establishment, that that has been true.